It's A
Kind Of
MAGIC

Mathematical Magic
Tricks Explained

David Crawford

Contents

Introduction

"How do you do that?" This must be one of the most satisfying things any magician (or would-be magician) can ever hear when the trick he/she has just performed has created a sense of awe and wonder among the members of their audience. However, to be a really good magician takes a lot of practice and, often, some very intricate equipment. In this book I will attempt to present some more mundane magical tricks based on mathematics which require no special skills on the part of the performer beyond the ability to carry out some arithmetical calculations but which can, nonetheless, still create the same sort of sense of wonder. Most of these tricks are ones I have used in the classroom as part of my teaching to try and engender enthusiasm for mental and written arithmetic and to provide a source of problems for my pupils to try and discover for themselves why the tricks work as well as just to provide a bit of mathematical entertainment.

What, I hope, makes this book a little different from many of the other books on mathematical or self-working magic is that I will be giving as much attention to why the tricks are working by presenting algebraic justifications for each trick as I will to explaining how to perform the tricks. I make no claims about the originality of the vast majority of the tricks presented here as most of them are ones I have gathered from different sources such as magic books, mathematical articles and the internet over the years. The rather haphazard way in which I have collected the tricks does make crediting their source a difficult task and, while I will acknowledge my source, when I know it, there will be some tricks whose origin I do not know and others where my source for the trick is not the original one. Where this is the case, I can only pass on my thanks to those unknown sources and hope that they will not object to seeing their ideas discussed here.

The field of mathematical magic has a long history, being first surveyed in depth more than 50 years ago by Martin Gardner in his seminal work "Mathematics, Magic and Mystery" (Gardner (1956)) and many of the tricks he presented there or in his later works will be considered here. The number tricks and puzzles of Canon D. B. Eperson that featured in his "Puzzles, Pastimes, Problems" columns in the Mathematics in School magazine also provided a good source for my teaching materials and I acknowledge a large debt to both these giants of the field.

The book itself is divided into two main sections: How (which explains how you can perform the tricks) and Why (which covers the mathematical explanations for the tricks and suggests how mathematics can be used to create similar tricks of your own). Within each of these, there are further sub-divisions into Number Tricks and Card Tricks where the different types of trick will be considered. The Number Trick section contains a variety of tricks ranging from the very simple, accessible to children of all ages, through to some that are either quite complicated to perform or are mathematically sophisticated and so complicated to explain. The Card Tricks section consists of a range of tricks that do not require any special manipulative skill or sleight of hand and, in the main, no setting up of the deck before the trick is started. Of course, this does not imply that you would not need to practise the tricks before carrying them out. Smooth presentation, which can only come with familiarity with a particular trick, will always be a bonus for any performer. As I mentioned earlier, all of these are tricks I have used within the classroom and, while I will generally refer to performing the tricks to an audience, a class full of pupils has proved to be an equally appropriate venue.

Of course, the tricks presented in this book just skim the surface of all the mathematically based tricks out there. For example, when I typed "number tricks" into Google, I got over 57 million hits (and so naturally I haven't looked at all of them!), while typing "mathematical card tricks" gave over two million hits, which means there is plenty of new material out there for those who feel inspired to discover more.

I hope you enjoy the tricks here and, most importantly for me, you and your audience enjoy the application of mathematics and, if so, perhaps some of you will feel inspired to take the subject further.

I would like to take this opportunity to thank the Mathematical Association for encouraging me to take the step from giving occasional talks on the subject to pulling all my resources together into this book and I would particularly like to thank Richard Kirby and Henry Langley for their meticulous proof-reading and useful comments. I would also like to thank two students of mine, Sarah Clay for working through the card tricks to test the clarity of my explanations and Tom Catterall for taking the photographs that show the card layout for a few of the card tricks. I also gratefully acknowledge the Graphics Factory (www.graphicsfactory.com) for permission to use the various images that illustrate this work. I would also like to thank the pupils of Leicester Grammar School who have been so willing to try out these tricks over the years and without whose enthusiasm I would not have kept searching for new ideas.

An Introductory Trick

- Choose any 2-digit number.
- Multiply it by 9.
- Add the digits of your answer together and repeat the addition of digits until you have a 1-digit number.
- Multiply your answer by 2.
- Find the cartoon numbers 1 to 8 somewhere on the pages of the book.
- Add together the page numbers on which these cartoon numbers appear.
- Subtract your previous answer from the total of the relevant page numbers.
- Divide your answer by 5.
- Turn to the page given by your final answer and look at the middle word of the title of the trick being explained there.

- I hope you find all the other tricks fall into this category as well.

How

To Perform

The Number

Tricks

Part A

And Your Answer Is

The tricks presented in this section are all designed so that a particular answer is obtained whatever values are initially chosen by the members of the audience. Tricks like this can be very simple, making them useable as quick mental arithmetic starters within the classroom, or more complex requiring pen and paper and an ability to follow directions accurately.

Number Trick A1

Think Of A Number (1)

The examples presented in this trick are some of the simplest ones to carry out, making them suitable for mental arithmetic practice in the classroom. The complexity of this type of trick can be varied according to the level of mathematical ability of your audience and is limited only by the algebraic manipulation skills of the person devising the particular example in the first place.

Version 1

• Tell your audience to think of a number (and remember it).	7
• Then tell them to double it.	$7 \times 2 = 14$
• Next tell them to add 10.	$14 + 10 = 24$
• Then tell them to halve their answer.	$24 \div 2 = 12$
• Finally, tell them to take away the number they first thought of.	$12 - 7 = 5$
• Reveal that their answer is 5.	

If you change the number you add, the final answer will also change. In this simple case, the final answer will be half the number added.

Version 2

• Tell your audience to think of a number (and remember it).	3
• Then tell them to double it.	$3 \times 2 = 6$
• Next tell them to add 6.	$6 + 6 = 12$
• Then tell them to double this answer.	$12 \times 2 = 24$
• Next tell them to add 4.	$24 + 4 = 28$
• Then tell them to divide their answer by 4.	$28 \div 4 = 7$
• Finally, tell them to take away the number they first thought of.	$7 - 3 = 4$
• Reveal that their answer is 4.	

Again, changing the numbers added will result in different final answers being obtained. To keep the arithmetic simple, involving only whole numbers, the first number added should be even and the second number added should be a multiple of 4. The final answer will then be ½ of the first number plus ¼ of the second number.

More complex examples with extra steps are possible but deciding upon general rules to keep the arithmetic simple becomes more involved and it is probably better to focus on specific cases rather than general examples.

Version 3

- Tell your audience to think of a number (and remember it).
- Then tell them to multiply it by 3.
- Next tell them to add 6.
- Then tell them to multiply this answer by 4.
- Next tell them to add 8.
- Then tell them to halve their answer.
- Next tell them to subtract 4.
- Then tell them to divide their answer by 6.
- Finally, tell them to take away the number they first thought of.
- Reveal that their answer is 2.

10

$10 \times 3 = 30$
$30 + 6 = 36$
$36 \times 4 = 144$
$144 + 8 = 152$
$152 \div 2 = 76$
$76 - 4 = 72$
$72 \div 6 = 12$

$12 - 10 = 2$

Number Trick A2

Think Of A Number (2)

In the previous trick, the examples were fairly straightforward requiring only addition, subtraction, multiplication and division to carry them out. Explaining why those examples worked was also a fairly straightforward process. The examples presented in this trick take things to another level numerically and algebraically with the introduction of squaring, cubing and square-rooting within the arithmetic steps and quadratic factorisation and algebraic division within the proofs. All of the versions here have been created to give the answer 2, but similar manipulations can be arranged to give other answers.

Version 1
- Tell your audience to think of a number above 2 (and remember it).
- Then tell them to square it.
- Next tell them to subtract 4.
- Then tell them to divide their answer by the number 2 less than their original number.
- Finally, tell them to take away the number they first thought of.
- Reveal that their answer is 2.

$$5$$
$$5^2 = 25$$
$$25 - 4 = 21$$
$$21 \div (5 - 2)$$
$$= 21 \div 3 = 7$$

$$7 - 5 = 2$$

Version 2
- Tell your audience to think of a number (and remember it).
- Then tell them to multiply it by the number 4 bigger than itself.
- Next tell them to add 4.
- Then tell them to find the square root of this answer. *This will need to be the negative square root of the answer if their original number was negative.*
- Finally, tell them to take away the number they first thought of.
- Reveal that their answer is 2.

$$6$$
$$6 \times (6 + 4)$$
$$= 6 \times 10 = 60$$
$$60 + 4 = 64$$
$$\sqrt{64} = 8$$

$$8 - 6 = 2$$

Version 3
- Tell your audience to think of a number (and remember it).
- Then tell them to multiply it by 4.
- Then tell them to multiply this answer by the number 1 above their original value.
- Next tell them to add 1.
- Then tell them to find the square root of their answer. *This will need to be the negative square root of the answer if their original number was negative.*
- Next tell them to subtract 1.
- Finally, tell them to divide their answer by their original number.
- Reveal that their answer is 2.

$$7$$
$$7 \times 4 = 28$$
$$28 \times (7 + 1)$$
$$= 28 \times 8 = 224$$
$$224 + 1 = 225$$
$$\sqrt{225} = 15$$

$$15 - 1 = 14$$

$$14 \div 7 = 2$$

Version 4

- Tell your audience to think of a number above 2 (and remember it).
- Then tell them to cube it.
- Next tell them to subtract 8.
- Then tell them to divide their answer by the number 2 less than their original number.
- Then tell them to add their original number.
- Then tell them to add their original number again.
- Next tell them to find the square root of their answer.
- Finally, tell them to take away the number they first thought of.
- Reveal that their answer is 2.

$$4$$
$$4^3 = 64$$
$$64 - 8 = 56$$
$$56 \div (4 - 2)$$
$$= 56 \div 2 = 28$$
$$28 + 4 = 32$$
$$32 + 4 = 36$$
$$\sqrt{36} = 6$$

$$6 - 4 = 2$$

Version 5

- Tell your audience to think of a number above 2 (and remember it).
- Then tell them to multiply it by the number 1 smaller than itself.
- Then tell them to multiply their answer by the number 1 bigger than their original number.
- Next tell them to add their original number.
- Then tell them to multiply their answer by 8.
- Next tell them to find the cube root of their answer.
- Finally, tell them to divide their answer by the number they first thought of.
- Reveal that their answer is 2.

$$5$$
$$5 \times (5 - 1)$$
$$= 5 \times 4 = 20$$
$$20 \times (5 + 1)$$
$$= 20 \times 6 = 120$$
$$120 + 5 = 125$$
$$125 \times 8 = 1000$$
$$\sqrt[3]{1000} = 10$$

$$10 \div 5 = 2$$

Version 6

- Tell your audience to think of a number (and remember it).
- Then tell them to double it
- Then tell them to square their answer.
- Then tell them to multiply their answer by the number 2 more than their current answer.

- Then tell them to add 1.
- Next tell them to find the square root of their answer.
- Then tell them to subtract 1.
- Next tell them to take the square root of their answer.
- Finally, tell them to divide their answer by the number they first thought of.
- Reveal that their answer is 2.

$$3$$
$$3 \times 2 = 6$$
$$6^2 = 36$$
$$36 \times (36 + 2)$$
$$= 36 \times 38$$
$$= 1368$$
$$1368 + 1 = 1369$$
$$\sqrt{1369} = 37$$
$$37 - 1 = 36$$
$$\sqrt{36} = 6$$

$$6 \div 3 = 2$$

Number Trick A3

Palindromic Puzzles

A palindrome is a word or phrase that reads the same from either end like the name "Hannah" or the phrase "was it a cat I saw". A palindromic number has exactly the same structure but with numbers instead of letters. Hence numbers like 343 and 1234321 are both palindromic numbers. The first three examples of palindromic number tricks are all taken from an issue of Canon D. B. Eperson's regular column "Puzzles, Pastimes, Problems" that featured in the Mathematics in School magazine for so many years (Eperson (1989)).

Version 1

- Tell your audience to write down a 3-digit palindromic number where the first 2 digits add to 7.

  616

- Tell them to divide their number by 7.

  $616 \div 7 = 88$

- Then tell them to divide their answer by 13 and find the remainder.

  $88 \div 13 = 6$ rem 10

- Reveal that their answer is 10.

  remainder is 10

Version 2

- Tell your audience to write down a 3-digit palindromic number where the first 2 digits add to 14.

  595

- Tell them to divide their number by 7.

  $595 \div 7 = 85$

- Then tell them to divide their answer by 13 and find the remainder.

  $85 \div 13 = 6$ rem 7

- Reveal that their answer is 7.

  remainder is 7

Version 3

- Tell your audience to write down a 3-digit palindromic number where the first 2 digits add to 13.

  676

- Tell them to divide their number by 13.

  $676 \div 13 = 52$

- Then tell them to divide their answer by 7 and find the remainder.

  $52 \div 7 = 7$ rem 3

- Reveal that their answer is 3.

  remainder is 3

Version 4

- Tell your audience to write down a 4-digit palindromic number where the first 2 digits add to 9.

- Tell them to divide their number by 11.
- Then tell them to divide their answer by 9.
- Tell them to divide this answer by 3 and find the remainder.
- Reveal that their answer is 1.

3663

$3663 \div 11 = 333$
$333 \div 9 = 37$
$37 \div 3 = 12 \text{ rem } 1$

remainder is 1

Number Trick A4

All The Twos

The different versions of the trick presented here are all examples of tricks where more than one value can be freely chosen but the result at the end of the calculations will still be the same for all. The mathematics involved is relatively straightforward (addition and division), although some of the later variants do require a very methodical approach to ensure possibilities are not missed.

Version 1	
• Ask your audience to write down three different 1-digit numbers.	2, 7, 5
• Using two of these digits at a time, tell them to form six different 2-digit numbers.	27, 25, 52, 57, 72, 75
• Now tell them to add up their six 2-digit numbers.	$27 + 25 + 52 + 57 + 72 + 75 = 308$
• Finally, tell them to divide their answer by the sum of their original three 1-digit numbers.	$308 \div (2 + 7 + 5)$ $= 308 \div 14 = 22$
• Reveal that their answer is 22.	

For younger pupils, limiting the numbers chosen to three different figures between 1 and 5 would mean that the maximum value they would need to divide by would be 12, making the arithmetic more accessible.

Version 2	
• Ask your audience to write down four different 1-digit numbers.	1, 3, 6, 9
• Using two of these digits at a time, tell them to form 12 different 2-digit numbers.	13, 16, 19, 31, 36, 39, 61, 63, 69, 91, 93, 96
• Now tell them to add up their 12 2-digit numbers.	$13 + 16 + 19 + 31 + 36 + 39 + 61 + 63 + 69 + 91 + 93 + 96 = 627$
• Finally, tell them to divide their answer by the sum of their original four 1-digit numbers.	$627 \div (1 + 3 + 6 + 9)$ $= 627 \div 19 = 33$
• Reveal that their answer is 33.	

To increase the challenge or to provide tricks suitable for calculator practice, larger numbers could be created as shown in versions 3 and 4 or larger numbers chosen initially as shown in version 5.

Version 3

- Ask your audience to write down three different 1-digit numbers.
- Using all of these digits each time, tell them to form six different 3-digit numbers.
- Now tell them to add up their six 3-digit numbers.

- Finally, tell them to divide their answer by the sum of their original three 1-digit numbers.
- Reveal that their answer is 222.

1, 5, 8

158, 185, 518, 581, 815, 851

$158 + 185 + 518 + 581 + 815 + 851 = 3108$

$3108 \div (1 + 5 + 8)$
$= 3108 \div 14 = 222$

Version 4

- Ask your audience to write down four different 1-digit numbers.
- Using all of these digits each time, tell them to form 24 different 3-digit numbers.

- Now tell them to add up their 24 3-digit numbers.

- Finally, tell them to divide their answer by the sum of their original four 1-digit numbers.
- Reveal that their answer is 666.

1, 3, 4, 8

134, 138, 143, 148, 183, 184, 314, 318, 341, 348, 381, 384, 413, 418, 431, 438, 481, 483, 813, 814, 831, 834, 841, 843

$134 + 138 + 143 + 148 + 183 + 184 + 314 + 318 + 341 + 348 + 381 + 384 + 413 + 418 + 431 + 438 + 481 + 483 + 813 + 814 + 831 + 834 + 841 + 843 = 10656$

$10656 \div (1 + 3 + 4 + 8)$
$= 10656 \div 16 = 666$

Version 5

- Ask your audience to write down three different 2-digit numbers.
- Using two of these 2-digit numbers at a time, tell them to form six different 4-digit numbers.
- Now tell them to add up their six 4-digit numbers.

- Finally, tell them to divide their answer by the sum of their original three 2-digit numbers.
- Reveal that their answer is 202.

13, 28, 43

1328, 1343, 2813, 2843, 4313, 4328

$1328 + 1343 + 2813 + 2843 + 4313 + 4328 = 16968$

$19698 \div (13 + 28 + 43)$
$= 16968 \div 84 = 202$

Number Trick A5

1089 And All That

This trick was put forward by professional mathematician David Acheson in his book of the same name (Acheson (2002)) as being the first piece of mathematics that really impressed him when he saw it as a boy. It is certainly surprising, given such a free choice of numbers, that only a few short steps will result in the same answer each time.

• Tell your audience to write down any 3-digit number whose first and last digits differ by more than 1*.	295
• Then tell them to reverse their number.	592
• Next tell them to subtract the smaller of the two 3-digit numbers from the larger.	$592 - 295 = 297$
• Finally, reverse this answer and add the reversed answer to the original answer of the subtraction.	$297 + 792$ $= 1089$
• Reveal that their answer is 1089.	

I often use this trick as a starting point for a further trick to spell out a message. The particular extension suggested here is one I've used near the end of the Christmas term at school.

• Tell your audience to carry out the calculations above without revealing that everyone should have obtained 1089.	1089
• Then tell them to multiply their answer by 100000.	1089×100000 $= 108900000$
• Then tell them to subtract 1135847.	$108900000 - 1135847 =$ 107764153
• Finally, tell them to replace the following numbers with these letters: 1 = M, 3 = S, 4 = X, 5 = A, 6 = Y, 7 = R, 0 = E and read the message.	MERRYXMAS

* The trick can be made to work even if the first and last digits of the chosen number differ by 1. In this case, the answer that is obtained after the subtraction step is 99 which must then be treated as the three figure number 099 before it is reversed.

If the basic trick is extended to 4-digit numbers where the first and the last digits differ by more than 1, there are actually 3 different possible outcomes depending on the relationship between the 2nd and 3rd digits.

• If the 2nd and 3rd digits are equal, you will obtain 10989.

- If the 2nd digit is more than the 3rd digit, you will get 10890.
- If the 2nd digit is less than the 3rd digit, you will get 9999.

These arrangements assume that the first digit in the original number is larger than the final digit. If the reverse is true then the second and third options are reversed.

Similar extensions are also possible when starting with a 5-digit number (such as abcde).

Assuming a > e, then if

      a) b = d, you will obtain 109989
      b) b > d, you will obtain 109890
      c) b < d, you will obtain 99099.

Number Trick A6

Ever Decreasing Numbers

This trick in its raw form is a simple exercise in subtraction and, as such, is suitable for use with relatively young children.

• Tell your audience to write down a 4-digit number whose digits are decreasing by one each time as the number is written.	7654
• Tell them to reverse the number.	4567
• Then tell them to subtract their reversed number from the original number.	$7654 - 4567$ $= 3087$
• Reveal that their answer is 3087.	

In a similar way to that described in the previous trick, this trick can be used as a basis for creating messages. An example of this is given below.

• Tell your audience to carry out the calculations above without revealing that everyone should have obtained 3087.	3087
• Then tell them to multiply their answer by 10.	$3087 \times 10 = 30870$
• Next tell them to subtract 16445.	$30870 - 16445 = 14225$
• Finally, tell them to replace the following numbers with these letters: 1 = O, 2 = E, 4 = L, 5 = H and then read the message from right to left.	OLLEH

Variations.
- If you start with a 3-digit number whose digits are decreasing by one each time, then the final answer is 198.

- If the digits of your number decrease by two each time as you read from left to right, then starting with a 3-digit number will give the answer 396 and starting with a 4-digit number will give the answer 6174*

* The number 6174 is known as Kaprekar's constant. This is the value that will eventually occur and then continue to occur if you apply the following rule to any 4-digit number whose digits are not all equal.

a) Arrange the digits in ascending order and in descending order and then subtract the smaller number from the larger.

b) Repeat this process with the answer obtained and continue until a constant value occurs. This will be 6174. (The 3-digit equivalent is 495.)

Number Trick A7
Dice, the Universe and Everything

In this trick, you need to judge the mathematical sophistication of your audience when giving your initial explanation of how to carry out the trick. For an older audience, they need to imagine rolling two normal 6-sided dice of different colours and form a sample space of the possible totals that can be obtained while a younger audience can simply be told to form an addition square.

- Tell your audience to form an addition square using the numbers 1 to 6 along the top and the side of the square.

+	1	2	3	4	5	6
1	2	3	4	5	6	7
2	3	4	5	6	7	8
3	4	5	6	7	8	9
4	5	6	7	8	9	10
5	6	7	8	9	10	11
6	7	8	9	10	11	12

- Tell them to choose any number inside the square, highlight it (shown here in grey but they can simply ring the number) and then cross out the other numbers in the same row and the same column.

+	1	2	3	4	5	6
1	2	3	4	5	6	7
2	3	4	5	6	7	8
3	4	5	6	7	8	9
4	5	6	7	8	9	10
5	6	7	8	9	10	11
6	7	8	9	10	11	12

- Then tell them to choose another number that is not highlighted or crossed out and highlight that number. Then cross out all the other numbers in the same row and the same column.

+	1	2	3	4	5	6
1	2	3	4	5	6	7
2	3	4	5	6	7	8
3	4	5	6	7	8	9
4	5	6	7	8	9	10
5	6	7	8	9	10	11
6	7	8	9	10	11	12

- Next tell them to repeat this process of highlighting a number and crossing out numbers until they have 6 highlighted values and the rest of the numbers are crossed out.

- Finally, tell them to add up the highlighted numbers.

$$3 + 7 + 7 + 10 + 8 + 7$$
$$= 42$$

- Reveal that their answer is 42*.

A slightly more impressive version of this trick is to present your audience with an addition square without the numbers used to form it and ask them to decide what numbers were used. They should be able to come up with different solutions but, if they carry out the trick as described above, they will all get the same magic value for that particular square (which you calculate in the way described on Page 141) even though the numbers they used to form the square were different.

* This value (42), according to the mega computer "Deep Thought" in the late science-fiction author Douglas Adams' book "The Hitch-Hikers' Guide to the Galaxy" (Adams (1979)) is the <u>answer</u> to Life, the Universe and Everything, although the exact details of the <u>question</u> remained unclear.

Number Trick A8

Multiplying Dice

For this trick you need two normal 6-sided dice for each person in your audience carrying out the trick.

- Tell your audience to roll two normal cubical dice.
- Then tell them to multiply the numbers on the tops of the dice.

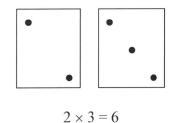

$2 \times 3 = 6$

- Next tell them to multiply the numbers on the bottoms of the dice.

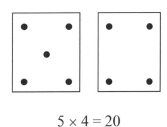

$5 \times 4 = 20$

- Then tell them to multiply the top number on the left hand die by the bottom number on the right hand die.

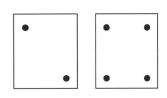

$2 \times 4 = 8$

- Next tell them to multiply the top number on the right hand die by the bottom number on the left hand die.

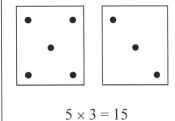

$5 \times 3 = 15$

- Finally, tell them to add the answers to their four multiplications together.
- Reveal that their answer is 49.

$6 + 20 + 8 + 15 = 49$

The key to this trick is that the opposite numbers on a cubical die add up to 7 and, by carrying out the multiplications and the final addition as shown, you have effectively multiplied 7 by 7. This means you can extend the trick to different dice, if you have any, provided the opposite numbers always add up to the same thing. Applying the trick to two octahedral dice where the opposite numbers add up to 9 will give you a total of 81, while using two icosahedral dice where the opposite numbers add up to 21 will give you a total of 441. Do check your dice carefully though – my dodecahedral dice, where the opposite numbers should add up to 13, are numbered very strangely with no constant relation between the numbers on opposite faces. You can even use two different type dice in the trick. For example, using a cubical die and an octahedral die will give a total of 63 (= 7 × 9).

Number Trick A9

A Prime Example

This is a very simple trick to state and to carry out, provided your audience know what a prime number is, but the proof is a little more complex.

• Tell your audience to think of a prime number above 3.	29
• Tell them to square it.	$29^2 = 841$
• Then tell them to add 17.	$841 + 17 = 858$
• Finally tell them to divide their answer by 12 and find the remainder.	$858 \div 12 = 71$ rem 6
• Reveal that their remainder is 6.	remainder is 6

A simpler version of the trick, where the division will be easier to do, would be to divide their answer after adding 17 by 4. In this case the remainder will always be 2.

Number Trick A10

Elephant!

This trick relies on the geographical knowledge of your audience as well as a mathematical property so, if you feel this is unlikely to be sufficient, you may need to help them out with a list from which they can choose.

• Tell your audience to think of a number.	14
• Then tell them to add 2.	$14 + 2 = 16$
• Next tell them to multiply their answer by 3.	$16 \times 3 = 48$
• Then tell them to add 6.	$48 + 6 = 54$
• Next tell them to multiply this answer by 3.	$54 \times 3 = 162$
• Then tell them to add the digits of their answer together and to repeat the process, if necessary, until they have a 1-digit answer.	$1 + 6 + 2 = 9$
• Next tell them to subtract 5.	$9 - 5 = 4$
• Then tell them to think of the letter that is in that position in the alphabet.	D
• Then tell them to think of a European country whose name begins with that letter. (This is where you may need a list of countries – one possible list is given below*).	Denmark
• Finally, ask them to think of a mammal whose name begins with the second letter of that country.	Elephant (probably!)
• Ask them "How long is its' trunk?" and wait for the look of surprise.	

* A – Austria; B – Belgium; C – Cyprus; D – Denmark; E – England; F – France; G – Greece; H – Hungary; I – Italy.

Number Trick A11

It's Magic!

This trick uses the same general mathematical property to force a particular answer as the previous trick. However, this one is perhaps simpler to use with a younger audience as it makes no assumptions about any general knowledge of the audience although it is longer and does seem to require more careful following. This version of the trick was one I found on the Internet submitted by Dr Mark Colyvan at http://owl.infosys.utas.edu.au/mathemagicians_circle/table4.html.

• Tell your audience to think of a number between 1 and 10.	7
• Then tell them to add their age in years.	$7 + 13 = 20$
• Then tell them to subtract the number of vowels in their first name.	$20 - 2 = 18$
• Next tell them to add the number of the month in which their birthday lies.	$18 + 6 = 24$
• If their result is a 2-digit number, they should add 2 to the final digit and use this for the next stage, otherwise they should add 1 to their previous answer.	$4 + 2 = 6$
• Next tell them to multiply their answer by 9.	$6 \times 9 = 54$
• Then tell them to add the digits of their answer together, repeating the process if necessary, until they have a 1-digit answer.	$5 + 4 = 9$
• Next tell them that if their answer is even they should add 2 but if their answer is odd, they should add 4.	$9 + 4 = 13$
• Then tell them to write down the letter that is in that position in the alphabet.	M
• Next tell them to subtract 12 and write down the corresponding letter.	$13 - 12 = 1$ A
• Then tell them to add 6 and write down the corresponding letter.	$1 + 6 = 7$ G
• Then tell them to add 2 and write down the corresponding letter.	$7 + 2 = 9$ I
• Then tell them to subtract 6 and write down the corresponding letter.	$9 - 6 = 3$ C
• Finally, tell them to read the word they've formed.	MAGIC

Part B

Back Where You Started

In this, the shortest of the number trick sections, I will be looking at some tricks that result in the initial value chosen reappearing as the answer at the final step or repeating a number of times to make the final answer. In the simpler cases, these tricks are very similar to the initial tricks in Section A but instead of taking away or dividing by the number initially thought of to leave a predicted value, a value will be removed to leave the initial value. Many of these tricks are based on items taken from the "Puzzles, Pastimes, Problems" series by Canon D. B. Eperson which appeared in Mathematics in School for so many years.

Number Trick B1

Back To The Beginning (1)

The versions of this trick are, as stated in the introduction, very similar to the first few tricks in Section A. Again the possible complexity of any similar trick you might want to devise yourself is only limited by the level of algebraic manipulation you want to apply when creating it. The versions presented here start from the very simple, which are suitable for mental arithmetic work with pupils of all ages, and build up in complexity.

Version 1
- Ask for a volunteer and tell them to think of a number.   7
- Tell them to double it. $7 \times 2 = 14$
- Then tell them to add 16. $14 + 16 = 30$
- Next tell them to halve their answer. $30 \div 2 = 15$
- Finally, tell them to subtract 8 to obtain their original value. $15 - 8 = 7$

Version 2
- Ask for a volunteer and tell them to think of a number.   3
- Tell them to double it. $3 \times 2 = 6$
- Then tell them to add 10. $6 + 10 = 16$
- Next tell them to double their answer again. $16 \times 2 = 32$
- Then tell them to add 8. $32 + 8 = 40$
- Next tell them to divide their answer by 4. $40 \div 4 = 10$
- Finally, tell them to subtract 7 to obtain their original value. $10 - 7 = 3$

Version 3
- Ask for a volunteer and tell them to think of a number.   10
- Tell them to multiply it by 3. $10 \times 3 = 30$
- Then tell them to add 2. $30 + 2 = 32$
- Next tell them to multiply their answer by 4. $32 \times 4 = 128$
- Then tell them to add 12. $128 + 12 = 140$
- Next tell them to halve their answer. $140 \div 2 = 70$
- Then tell them to subtract 4. $70 - 4 = 66$
- Next tell them to divide their answer by 6. $66 \div 6 = 11$
- Finally, tell them to subtract 1 to obtain their original value. $11 - 1 = 10$

Number Trick B2

Back To The Beginning (2)

The versions presented as part of this trick are more complex to prove algebraically and more difficult for pupils to perform mentally than those in the previous trick as they involve squaring and finding square roots of numbers. It might, therefore, be useful for anyone trying the tricks to have a calculator available to speed up the tricks and allow larger values to be chosen. Some of these versions are very similar, apart from the final step, to those presented in Number Trick A2.

Version 1

- Ask for a volunteer and tell them to think of a number greater than 2.
- Tell them to square it.
- Then tell them to subtract 4.
- Next tell them to divide their answer by the number 2 less than their original number.
- Finally, tell them to subtract 2 to obtain their original value.

$$7$$
$$7^2 = 49$$
$$49 - 4 = 45$$
$$45 \div (7 - 2)$$
$$= 45 \div 5 = 9$$

$$9 - 2 = 7$$

Version 2

- Ask for a volunteer and tell them to think of a number.
- Tell them to multiply it by the number 4 more than their original number.
- Then tell them to add 4.
- Next tell them to find the square root of their answer.
- Finally, tell them to subtract 2 to obtain their original value.

$$4$$
$$4 \times (4 + 4)$$
$$= 4 \times 8 = 32$$
$$32 + 4 = 36$$
$$\sqrt{36} = 6$$

$$6 - 2 = 4$$

Version 3

- Ask for a volunteer and tell them to think of a number.
- Tell them to multiply it by 4.
- Then tell them to multiply their answer by the number 1 greater than their original number.
- Next tell them to add 1.
- Then tell them to find the square root of their answer.
- Next tell them to subtract 1.
- Finally, tell them to divide their answer by 2 to obtain their original value.

$$5$$
$$5 \times 4 = 20$$
$$20 \times (5 + 1)$$
$$= 20 \times 6$$
$$= 120$$
$$120 + 1 = 121$$
$$\sqrt{121} = 11$$

$$11 - 1 = 10$$

$$10 \div 2 = 5$$

Version 4

- Ask for a volunteer and tell them to think of a number.

5

- Tell them to square it.

$5^2 = 25$

- Then tell them to add 6 times their original number.

$25 + 6 \times 5$
$= 25 + 30$
$= 55$

- Next tell them to add 9.

$55 + 9 = 64$

- Then tell them to find the square root of their answer.

$\sqrt{64} = 8$

- Finally, tell them to subtract 3 to obtain their original value.

$8 - 3 = 5$

Version 5

- Ask for a volunteer and tell them to think of a number greater than 2.

8

- Tell them to cube it.

$8^3 = 512$

- Then tell them to subtract 8.

$512 - 8 = 504$

- Next tell them to divide their answer by the number 2 less than their original number.

$504 \div (8 - 2)$
$= 504 \div 6$
$= 84$

- Then tell them to add their original number.

$84 + 8 = 92$

- Next tell them to add their original number again.

$92 + 8 = 100$

- Then tell them to find the square root of their answer.

$\sqrt{100} = 10$

- Finally, tell them to subtract 2 to obtain their original value.

$10 - 2 = 8$

26

Number Trick B3

Digit Addition

The versions of this trick differ from those in the previous two tricks in that a crucial extra step involving the addition of the digits of an answer obtained is required to obtain the final answer. Some of the specific versions presented here come from one of Canon Eperson's columns (Eperson (1989)), while some are modifications of my own.

Version 1
- Ask for a volunteer and tell them to think of a number from 1 to 10 inclusive.
- Tell them to add 9.
- Finally, tell them to add the digits of their answer to obtain their original value.

$$8$$
$$8 + 9 = 17$$
$$1 + 7 = 8$$

Version 2
- Ask for a volunteer and tell them to think of a number between 2 and 11 inclusive.
- Tell them to add 9.
- Then tell them to double their answer.
- Next tell them to subtract their original number.
- Finally, tell them to add the digits of their answer to obtain their original value.

$$5$$
$$5 + 9 = 14$$
$$14 \times 2 = 28$$
$$28 - 5 = 23$$

$$2 + 3 = 5$$

Version 3
- Ask for a volunteer and tell them to think of a number between 2 and 10 inclusive.
- Tell them to add 6.
- Then tell them to multiply their answer by 3.
- Next tell them to subtract their original number.
- Then tell them to divide their answer by 2.
- Finally, tell them to add the digits of their answer to obtain their original value.

$$8$$
$$8 + 6 = 14$$
$$14 \times 3 = 42$$
$$42 - 8 = 34$$

$$34 \div 2 = 17$$

$$1 + 7 = 8$$

Version 4
- Ask for a volunteer and tell them to think of a number between 1 and 10 inclusive.
- Tell them to add 3.
- Then tell them to double their answer.
- Next tell them to add 3 again.
- Then tell them to subtract their original number.
- Finally, tell them to add the digits of their answer to obtain their original value.

$$5$$
$$5 + 3 = 8$$
$$8 \times 2 = 16$$
$$16 + 3 = 19$$
$$19 - 5 = 14$$

$$1 + 4 = 5$$

Version 5
- Ask for a volunteer and tell them to think of a number between 3 and 12 inclusive.   7
- Tell them to add 20. $7 + 20 = 27$
- Then tell them to multiply their answer by 3. $27 \times 3 = 81$
- Next tell them to subtract their original number. $81 - 7 = 74$
- Then tell them to halve their answer. $74 \div 2 = 37$
- Next tell them to subtract 3. $37 - 3 = 34$
- Finally, tell them to add the digits of their answer to obtain their original value. $3 + 4 = 7$

Version 6
- Ask for a volunteer and tell them to think of a number between 10 and 19 inclusive.   12
- Tell them to add 70. $12 + 70 = 82$
- Then tell them to multiply their answer by 10. $82 \times 10 = 820$
- Next tell them to add 2. $820 + 2 = 822$
- Finally, tell them to add the digits of their answer to obtain their original value. $8 + 2 + 2 = 12$

Version 7
- Ask for a volunteer and tell them to think of a number between 20 and 29.   27
- Tell them to add 60. $27 + 60 = 87$
- Next tell them to add the digits of their answer. $8 + 7 = 15$
- Finally, tell them to add 12 to obtain their original value. $15 + 12 = 27$

Number Trick B4

Digit Subtraction

The versions presented in this trick are similar to the ones in the previous trick except that some subtraction of digits instead of addition is required to produce the original number. As with the previous trick, most of the versions here come from one of Canon Eperson's columns (Eperson (1990)).

Version 1
- Ask for a volunteer and tell them to think of a number.
- Tell them to double it.
- Then tell them to add 7.
- Next tell them to multiply their answer by 5.
- Then tell them to subtract 2.
- Finally, tell them to subtract the units digit of their answer from the digits making up the rest of their answer to obtain their original value.

$$8$$
$$8 \times 2 = 16$$
$$16 + 7 = 23$$
$$23 \times 5 = 115$$
$$115 - 2 = 113$$
$$11 - 3 = 8$$

Version 2
- Ask for a volunteer and tell them to think of a number.
- Tell them to double it.
- Then tell them to add 3.
- Next tell them to multiply their answer by 5.
- Then tell them to subtract 4.
- Finally, tell them to subtract the units digit of their answer from the digits making up the rest of their answer to obtain their original value.

$$16$$
$$16 \times 2 = 32$$
$$32 + 3 = 35$$
$$35 \times 5 = 175$$
$$175 - 4 = 171$$
$$17 - 1 = 16$$

Version 3
- Ask for a volunteer and tell them to think of a number.
- Tell them to multiply it by 3.
- Then tell them to add 6.
- Next tell them to multiply their answer by 3.
- Then tell them to add 8.
- Next tell them to add their original number.
- Then tell them to subtract 4.
- Finally, tell them to subtract the units digit of their answer from the digits making up the rest of their answer to obtain their original value.

$$15$$
$$15 \times 3 = 45$$
$$45 + 6 = 51$$
$$51 \times 3 = 153$$
$$153 + 8 = 161$$
$$161 + 15 = 176$$
$$176 - 4 = 172$$
$$17 - 2 = 15$$

Number Trick B5

Multiply Up And Divide Down

Versions of this trick are very simple to devise, but they can provide neat self-checking problems in multiplication and division for use in the classroom.

Version 1

- Ask for a volunteer and tell them to think of a number.   8
- Tell them to multiply it by 3. $8 \times 3 = 24$
- Then tell them to multiply their answer by 5. $24 \times 5 = 120$
- Next tell them to add their original number. $120 + 8 = 128$
- Then tell them to divide their answer by 2. $128 \div 2 = 64$
- Finally, tell them to divide their answer by 8 to obtain their original value. $64 \div 8 = 8$

Version 2

- Ask for a volunteer and tell them to think of a number.   12
- Tell them to multiply it by 9. $12 \times 9 = 108$
- Then tell them to multiply their answer by 7. $108 \times 7 = 756$
- Next tell them to add their original number. $756 + 12 = 768$
- Then tell them to divide their answer by 2. $768 \div 2 = 384$
- Next tell them to divide their answer by 4. $384 \div 4 = 96$
- Finally, tell them to divide their answer by 8 to obtain their original value. $96 \div 8 = 12$

Version 3

- Ask for a volunteer and tell them to think of a number.   8
- Tell them to multiply it by 7. $8 \times 7 = 56$
- Then tell them to multiply their answer by 5. $56 \times 5 = 280$
- Next tell them to multiply their answer by 3. $280 \times 3 = 840$
- Then tell them to subtract their original number. $840 - 8 = 832$
- Next tell them to divide their answer by 2. $832 \div 2 = 416$
- Then tell them to divide their answer by 4. $416 \div 4 = 104$
- Finally, tell them to divide their answer by 13 to obtain their original value. $104 \div 13 = 8$

Number Trick B6

Repeating Sequences (1)

The versions of this trick are designed to produce repeating sequences of the number originally chosen and are, as with the previous trick, good sources of self-checking long multiplication problems for use in the classroom. Some of these versions here come from another of Canon Eperson's columns (Eperson (1985)).

Version 1
- Ask for a volunteer and tell them to think of a 1-digit number.
- Tell them to multiply it by 37.
- Finally, tell them to multiply their answer by 3 to obtain their original value repeated three times.

$$5$$
$$5 \times 37 = 185$$
$$185 \times 3 = 555$$

Version 2
- Ask for a volunteer and tell them to think of a 1-digit number.
- Tell them to multiply it by 271.
- Finally, tell them to multiply their answer by 41 to obtain their original value repeated five times.

$$4$$
$$4 \times 271 = 1084$$
$$1084 \times 41 = 44444$$

Version 3
- Ask for a volunteer and tell them to think of a 1-digit number.
- Tell them to multiply it by 37.
- Next tell them to multiply their answer by 13.
- Then tell them to multiply their answer by 11.
- Next tell them to multiply their answer by 7.
- Finally, tell them to multiply their answer by 3 to obtain their original value repeated six times.

$$7$$
$$7 \times 37 = 259$$
$$259 \times 13 = 3367$$
$$3367 \times 11 = 37037$$
$$37037 \times 7 = 259259$$
$$259259 \times 3 = 777777$$

Version 4
- Ask for a volunteer and tell them to think of a 1-digit number.
- Tell them to multiply it by 12345679.
- Finally, tell them to multiply their answer by 9 to obtain their original value repeated nine times.

$$4$$
$$4 \times 12345679 = 49382716$$
$$49382716 \times 9 = 444444444$$

Version 5

- Ask for a volunteer and tell them to think of a 2-digit number.
- Tell them to multiply it by 37.
- Next tell them to multiply their answer by 13.
- Then tell them to multiply their answer by 7.
- Finally, tell them to multiply their answer by 3 to obtain their original value repeated three times.

14
$14 \times 37 = 518$
$518 \times 13 = 6734$
$6734 \times 7 = 47138$
$47138 \times 3 = 141414$

Version 6

- Ask for a volunteer and tell them to think of a 3-digit number.
- Tell them to multiply it by 13.
- Next tell them to multiply their answer by 11.
- Finally, tell them to multiply their answer by 7 to obtain their original value repeated twice.

329
$329 \times 13 = 4277$
$4277 \times 11 = 47047$
$47047 \times 7 = 329329$

Of course, all these problems could be reversed to involve division instead of multiplication as the version shown below illustrates.

Version 7

- Ask for a volunteer and tell them to think of a 1-digit number.
- Tell them to write this figure down six times to produce a 6-digit number.
- Then tell them to divide their number by 3.
- Next tell them to divide their answer by 7.
- Then tell them to divide their answer by 11.
- Next tell them to divide their number by 13.
- Finally, tell them to divide their answer by 37 to obtain their original value.

8
888888
$888888 \div 3 = 296296$
$296296 \div 7 = 42328$
$42328 \div 11 = 3848$
$3848 \div 13 = 296$
$296 \div 37 = 8$

Number Trick B7

Repeating Sequences (2)

The versions presented in this trick are very similar to those presented in the previous trick except that an extra step is required to produce the full repetition.

Version 1
- Ask for a volunteer and tell them to think of a 1-digit number.
- Tell them to multiply it by 16.
- Next tell them to multiply their answer by 7.
- Finally, tell them to subtract their original number to obtain their original value repeated three times.

9

$9 \times 16 = 144$
$144 \times 7 = 1008$

$1008 - 9 = 999$

Version 2
- Ask for a volunteer and tell them to think of a 1-digit number.
- Tell them to multiply it by 139.
- Then tell them to multiply their answer by 8.
- Finally, tell them to subtract their original number to obtain their original value repeated four times.

7

$7 \times 139 = 973$
$973 \times 8 = 7784$

$7784 - 7 = 7777$

Version 3
- Ask for a volunteer and tell them to think of a 1-digit number.
- Tell them to multiply it by 463.
- Next tell them to multiply their answer by 8.
- Then tell them to multiply their answer by 3.
- Finally, tell them to subtract their original number to obtain their original value repeated five times.

6

$6 \times 463 = 2278$
$2278 \times 8 = 22224$
$22224 \times 3 = 66672$

$66672 - 6 = 66666$

Version 4
- Ask for a volunteer and tell them to think of a 1-digit number.
- Tell them to multiply it by 43.
- Next tell them to multiply their answer by 19.
- Then tell them to multiply their answer by 17.
- Next tell them to multiply their answer by 8.
- Finally, tell them to subtract their original value to obtain their original value repeated six times.

5

$5 \times 43 = 215$
$215 \times 19 = 4085$

$4085 \times 17 = 69445$

$69445 \times 8 = 555560$

$555560 - 5 = 555555$

Version 5

- Ask for a volunteer and tell them to think of a 2-digit number.

  38

- Tell them to multiply it by 17.

  $38 \times 17 = 646$

- Next tell them to multiply their answer by 6.

  $646 \times 6 = 3876$

- Finally, tell them to subtract their original value to obtain their original value repeated twice.

  $3876 - 38 = 3838$

Number Trick B8

A Magic Number

This trick works for any 4-digit number, but you can present it as if your volunteer has chosen a very special number and so has magic powers.

- Ask for a volunteer and tell them to think of any 4-digit number.

  2573

- Tell them to write down the first digit of their number.

  2

- Then tell them to write down the first 2 digits of their number.

  25

- Next tell them to write down the first 3 digits of their number.

  257

- Then tell them to add up the 3 numbers they have written down.

  $2 + 25 + 257 = 284$

- Next tell them to multiply their answer by 9.

  $284 \times 9 = 2556$

- Finally, tell them to add the sum of the digits of their original number to their answer to obtain their original number.

  $2556 + 2 + 5 + 7 + 3 = 2573$

Simpler (or harder versions) of the same basic trick can be performed by decreasing (or increasing) the number of digits of the original number chosen. The only difference will be that fewer (or more) different numbers using the first digits of the original number will need to be written down before addition and multiplication by 9 occur.

Number Trick B9

Number Reversal

The versions shown here are examples of a very simple number trick requiring only subtraction and a little number manipulation.

Version 1

• Ask for a volunteer and tell them to think of any 2-digit number with the first digit 3 more than the last digit.	85
• Tell them to subtract 27.	$85 - 27 = 58$
• Finally, tell them to reverse the digits of their answer to obtain their original number.	85

To change this trick, alter the difference between the digits of the original 2-digit number you tell your volunteer to choose and then change the subtracted number to 9 times that difference.

Version 2

• Ask for a volunteer and tell them to think of any 3-digit number with the first digit 3 more than the last digit.	734
• Tell them to subtract 297.	$734 - 297 = 437$
• Finally, tell them to reverse the digits of their answer to obtain their original number.	734

To change this trick, alter the difference between the digits of the original 3-digit number you tell your volunteer to choose and then change the subtracted number to 99 times that difference.

Further extensions are possible, but more steps are involved and the extra restrictions on the original number need to be applied.

Version 3

• Ask for a volunteer and tell them to think of any 4-digit number with the first digit 3 more than the last digit and the second digit 2 more than the third.	8755
• Tell them to subtract 2997.	$8755 - 2997 = 5758$
• Next tell them to subtract 180.	$5758 - 180 = 5578$
• Finally, tell them to reverse the digits of their answer to obtain their original number.	8755

To change this trick, alter the difference between the first and last digits of the original 4-digit number you tell your volunteer to choose and then change the first number subtracted to 999 times that difference and change the difference between the second and third digits and tell them to subtract 90 times that difference as the second subtracted number.

Part C
Mind Reading Tricks

The tricks in this section do not produce the same answer for everyone like the tricks in part A or return to the original value like those in part B. Instead, each number or set of numbers chosen by your volunteers will lead to a different answer and this is where you will use your "mind reading" skills to determine exactly what value or values had been thought of. Obviously you are not actually doing any mind reading, but the effect of turning the volunteers' seemingly unconnected answers back to their original values can be a very effective trick. Certainly when I use tricks like these in my classroom, I usually find that all my pupils want to have their values interpreted and, if they find my interpretation does not match their initial value, they are invariably keen to repeat their calculations until interpretation and initial value do match.

The first few tricks I will be presenting here are all fairly short and mainly rely on repeated multiplications by 2, 5 and 10 to shift values from one column to another. However, some of the later tricks are more intricate, requiring more mathematical effort on the part of the volunteer and, in some cases, more secret steps on the part of the performer before the initial value/values chosen can be revealed.

Number Trick C1

One Number Tricks

Simple tricks like these can be very useful in a classroom situation as a source of mental arithmetic examples and can provide opportunities for pupils to try and spot the links between the final answers and the original values chosen. Depending on the age and the level of mathematical sophistication your pupils possess, there is also the opportunity for them to try and prove <u>why</u> the tricks are working by using algebra.

Version 1

• Ask for a volunteer and tell them to think of a number.	16
• Then tell them to double it.	$2 \times 16 = 32$
• Next tell them to add 3.	$32 + 3 = 35$
• Then tell them to multiply by 5.	$35 \times 5 = 175$
• Finally, tell them to subtract 4.	$175 - 4 = 171$
• Ask them for their answer.	171
• **Secret Step: Subtract the units digit of their answer from the rest of their answer. Then reveal the number they chose.**	**$17 - 1 = 16$** **They chose 16**

Version 2

• Ask for a volunteer and tell them to think of an odd number.	7
• Then tell them to multiply it by 3.	$3 \times 7 = 21$
• Next tell them to add 1.	$21 + 1 = 22$
• Then tell them to multiply by 3 again.	$22 \times 3 = 66$
• Next tell them to halve their answer.	$66 \div 2 = 33$
• Finally, tell them to divide their answer by 9, ignoring any remainder.	$33 \div 9 = 3$ rem 6
• Ask them for their answer.	3
• **Secret Step: Double their answer and add 1. Then reveal the number they chose.**	**$2 \times 3 + 1 = 7$** **They chose 7**

Version 3

• Ask for a volunteer and tell them to think of a 2-digit number whose digits add to 11.	65
• Then tell them to add 2 lots of the first digit.	$65 + 2 \times 6 = 77$
• Next tell them to divide by 11.	$77 \div 11 = 7$
• Ask them for their answer.	7
• **Secret Step: Subtract 1 from their answer to get the tens digit of their number. Subtract this tens digit from 11 to get the units digit of their number. Then reveal the number they chose.**	**$7 - 1 = 6$** **$11 - 6 = 5$** **They chose 65**

Version 4

- Ask for a volunteer and tell them to think of a number between 1 and 9 inclusive.
- Then tell them to multiply it by 10.
- Next tell them to add their original number.
- Then tell them to multiply it by 3.
- Next tell them to multiply it by 11.
- Finally, tell them to multiply it by 3 again.
- Ask them for the final digit of their answer.
- **Secret Step: Subtract the number they tell you from 10 to get the number they chose. Reveal the number they chose.**
- **You can also reveal their full answer as their 1st digit is the number they chose, their 2nd digit is their 1st digit − 1 and their 3rd digit is the answer they told you − 1.**

$$6$$

$$6 \times 10 = 60$$
$$60 + 6 = 66$$
$$66 \times 3 = 198$$
$$198 \times 11 = 2178$$
$$2178 \times 3 = 6534$$
$$4$$

$$10 - 4 = 6$$
They chose 6
1st digit is 6
2nd digit is 6 − 1 = 5
3rd digit is 4 − 1 = 3
Full answer is 6534

Version 5

- Ask for a volunteer and tell them to choose a 2-digit number.
- Then tell them to multiply it by 43.
- Next tell them to multiply their answer by 7.
- Ask them for their answer, leaving off the last 2 digits.
- **Secret Step: Divide the number they tell you by 3. Then reveal the number they chose.**

$$27$$

$$27 \times 43 = 1161$$
$$1161 \times 7 = 8127$$
$$81$$

$$81 \div 3 = 27$$

They chose 27

Number Trick C2

Two Number Tricks

This type of trick is just as simple to perform as the previous type but, by introducing two variables, you make the task of spotting how you are using your volunteer's answer to discover their hidden values a more challenging one.

Version 1

- Ask for a volunteer and tell them to think of two numbers under 10.   6, 9
- Then tell them to multiply one number by 2. $2 \times 6 = 12$
- Next tell them to add 3. $12 + 3 = 15$
- Then tell them to multiply by 5. $15 \times 5 = 75$
- Finally, tell them to add the second number. $75 + 9 = 84$
- Ask them for their answer.   84
- **Secret Step: Subtract 15 from their answer to get a 2-digit number containing their two values. Then reveal the numbers they chose.**

$84 - 15 = 69$
They chose 6 and 9

Version 2

- Ask for a volunteer and tell them to think of two numbers under 10.   7, 3
- Then tell them to subtract 2 from the larger number. $7 - 2 = 5$
- Next tell them to multiply by 5. $5 \times 5 = 25$
- Then tell them to add the smaller of their original two numbers. $25 + 3 = 28$
- Next tell them to multiply by 2. $28 \times 2 = 56$
- Then tell them to add 9. $56 + 9 = 65$
- Finally, tell them to subtract the smaller of their original two numbers. $65 - 3 = 62$
- Ask them for their answer.   62
- **Secret Step: Add 1 to each digit of their answer to get their two numbers. Then reveal the number they chose.**

$6 + 1 = 7$
$2 + 1 = 3$
They chose 7 and 3

Version 3

- Ask for a volunteer and tell them to think of two numbers under 10.   7, 4
- Then tell them to add them together. $7 + 4 = 11$
- Next tell them to multiply by 10. $11 \times 10 = 110$
- Then tell them to add the larger of their original two numbers. $110 + 7 = 117$
- Finally, tell them to subtract the smaller of their original two numbers. $117 - 4 = 113$
- Ask them for their answer.   113

- **Secret Step: Subtract the units digit of their answer from the rest of their answer and halve the result. This is their smaller number. Add the units digit of their answer to the rest of their answer and halve the result. This is their larger number. Then reveal the number they chose.**

$11 - 3 = 8$
$8 \div 2 = 4$

$11 + 3 = 14$
$14 \div 2 = 7$

They chose 4 and 7

Version 4

- Ask for a volunteer and tell them to think of two numbers, one under 10 and one between 11 and 50.
- Then tell them to add their two numbers.
- Next tell them to multiply by 5.
- Then tell them to add the smaller of their original two numbers.
- Next tell them to multiply by 2.
- Then tell them to subtract the smaller of their original two numbers.
- Finally, tell them to subtract 1.
- Ask them for their answer.
- **Secret Step: Add 1 to the final digit of their answer to get their smaller number. Subtract this smaller number from the rest of their answer to get their larger number. Then reveal the numbers they chose.**

9, 43

$9 + 43 = 52$
$52 \times 5 = 260$
$260 + 9 = 269$

$269 \times 2 = 538$
$538 - 9 = 529$

$529 - 1 = 528$
528

$8 + 1 = 9$
$52 - 9 = 43$

They chose 9 and 43

Version 5

- Ask for a volunteer and tell them to choose two numbers, one under 10 and one over 10.
- Tell them to find the difference between them.
- Then multiply that difference by 10.
- Next tell them to add the smaller of their original two numbers.
- Then tell them to subtract 1.
- Ask them for their answer.
- **Secret Step: Add 1 to the units digit of their answer to get their smaller number. Add this smaller number to the rest of their answer to get their larger number. Then reveal the numbers they chose.**

5, 17

$17 - 5 = 12$

$12 \times 10 = 120$
$120 + 5 = 125$

$125 - 1 = 124$
124
$4 + 1 = 5$

$12 + 5 = 17$
They chose 5 and 17

Number Trick C3

Birthday Tricks

These tricks are very similar to the ones shown in the previous trick except that in these particular tricks, the aim is to discover dates of birthdays and so no restrictions on the size of the numbers being chosen are explicitly stated.

Version 1

• Ask for a volunteer and tell them to think of the number of the month in which they were born.	Born on 16th March 3
• Then tell them to multiply this by 5.	$3 \times 5 = 15$
• Next tell them to add 6.	$15 + 6 = 21$
• Then tell them to multiply by 4.	$21 \times 4 = 84$
• Next tell them to add 9.	$84 + 9 = 93$
• Then tell them to multiply by 5 again.	$93 \times 5 = 465$
• Finally, tell them to add the number of the date within the month when they were born.	$465 + 16 = 481$
• Ask them for their answer.	481
• **Secret Step: Subtract 165 from their answer. The final two digits of your result tell you the date they were born and the rest of your result tells you the month. Then reveal their birthday.**	**481 – 165 = 316** **date is 16th** **month is 3 $\equiv$ March** **Birthday is 16th March**

Version 2

• Ask for a volunteer and tell them to think of the number of the month in which they were born.	Born on 3rd July 7
• Then tell them to multiply this by 2.	$7 \times 2 = 14$
• Next tell them to add 5.	$14 + 5 = 19$
• Then tell them to multiply by 50.	$19 \times 50 = 950$
• Next tell them to add the number of the date within the month when they were born.	$950 + 3 = 953$
• Finally, tell them to subtract 365 for the days of a year.	$953 – 365 = 588$
• Ask them for their answer.	588
• **Secret Step: Add 115 to their answer. The final two digits of your result tell you the date they were born and the rest of your result tells you the month. Then reveal their birthday.**	**588 + 115 = 703** **date is 3rd** **month is 7 $\equiv$ July** **Birthday is 3rd July**

Number Trick C4

Age Finder

Version 1

- Ask for a volunteer and tell them to think of a number from 1 to 9*.
- Then tell them to multiply this number by 9.
- Next tell them to subtract their answer from 10 times their age.
- Finally, tell them to subtract 1.
- Ask them for their answer.
- **Secret Step: Add 1 to the units digit of their answer to get the number they chose. Add this number to the rest of their answer to get their age. Then reveal their age.**

Age 13

4

$4 \times 9 = 36$

$10 \times 13 - 36 = 94$

$94 - 1 = 93$

93

$3 + 1 = 4$

$9 + 4 = 13$

Their age is 13

*If your volunteer looks between 6 and 10, tell them to think of a number between 1 and 5 initially. If they look younger than this, do not try this trick!

Version 2a (for a person older than you.)

- Subtract your age from 99.

- Tell your volunteer this value and ask them to add it to their age.
- Then tell them to remove the left hand digit of their answer and then add it to the rest of their answer.
- Ask them for their answer.
- **Secret Step: Add your age to their answer to get their age. Then reveal their age.**

Assume you are 26 and your volunteer is 37

$99 - 26 = 73$

$73 + 37 = 110$

$10 + 1 = 11$

11

$11 + 26 = 37$

Their age is 37

Version 2b (for a person younger than you.)

- Add your age to 99.

- Tell your volunteer this value and ask them to subtract their age from it.
- Then tell them to remove the left hand digit of their answer and then add it to the rest of their answer.
- Ask them for their answer.
- **Secret Step: Subtract their answer from your age to get their age. Then reveal their age.**

Assume you are 26 and your volunteer is 12

$99 + 26 = 125$

$125 - 12 = 113$

$13 + 1 = 14$

14

$26 - 14 = 12$

Their age is 12

Number Trick C5

Scramble

• Ask for a volunteer and tell them to write down a 4-digit number.	2518
• Then tell them to rearrange the digits in their number to get a different 4-digit number.	8125
• Next tell them to subtract the smaller of their numbers from the larger.	$8125 - 2518 = 5607$
• Finally, tell them to cross out one non-zero digit in their answer and then rearrange the remaining digits.	cross out $6 \rightarrow 507$ rearrange $\rightarrow 750$
• Ask them for their final result.	750
• **Secret Step:** **Add the digits of their answer, repeating the process with your answer, if necessary, until you have a 1-digit result. Subtract this result from 9 to get the number crossed out (unless your result is 9 which means they crossed out a 9). Reveal the digit crossed out.**	$7 + 5 + 0 = 12$ $1 + 2 = 3$ $9 - 3 = 6$ **a 6 was crossed out**

This trick does not have to be restricted to 4-digit numbers, although using a 4-digit number or larger will make it harder for your audience to spot how you are performing the trick.

A very similar trick, which works for exactly the same mathematical reason, is to ask your volunteer to add the digits of the number they write down and then subtract that result from their original number before crossing out one digit of their answer. Your secret step will then be identical.

Number Trick C6

Consecutive Numbers

Although this trick and its variants rely on multiplication, they are rather different from the earlier ones in the section in that the shifting of values from one column to another does not use multiplication by 2, 5 and 10 but uses multiplication by larger values. I found the first version given here described on the excellent NRICH website (www.nrich.maths.org.uk), which is a great source of mathematical puzzles and, as the name suggests, enriching mathematical material for people of all ages. As the "mind reading" step is quite simple to perform, this trick can be carried out with a whole group who will get different answers depending on their initial choice of numbers but you will rapidly be able to tell them the values they initially chose.

Version 1

- Tell your audience to write down three consecutive numbers under 60.

  27, 28, 29

- Then tell them to add their numbers up.

  $27 + 28 + 29 = 84$

- Next ask someone in the audience to shout out a multiple of 3 under 100.

  45

- **Secret Step: Divide this number by 3 in your head and remember the value you get.**

  $45 \div 3 = 15$

- Then tell your audience to add the called out number to their total.

  $84 + 45 = 129$

- Finally, tell them to multiply their answer by 67.

  $129 \times 67 = 8643$

- Ask individual members of the audience for the last two digits of their answer.

  43

- **Secret Step: Subtract the number you remembered earlier from the result they give you. This will be the middle value of the three consecutive numbers chosen. Reveal the three numbers chosen.**

  $43 - 15 = 28$
  They chose 27, 28 and 29

Version 2

• Tell your audience to write down three consecutive numbers under 33.	15, 16, 17
• Then tell them to add their numbers up.	$15 + 16 + 17 = 48$
• Next ask someone in the audience to shout out a multiple of 3 under 50.	33
• **Secret Step: Divide this number by 3 in your head and remember the value you get.**	$\mathbf{33 \div 3 = 11}$
• Then tell your audience to add the called out number to their total.	$48 + 33 = 81$
• Finally, tell them to multiply their answer by 34.	$81 \times 34 = 2754$
• Ask individual members of the audience for the last two digits of their answer.	$81 \times 34 = 2754$
• **Secret Step: Divide the result they give you by 2 and then subtract the number you remembered earlier. This will be the middle value of the three consecutive numbers chosen. Reveal the three numbers chosen.**	$\mathbf{54 \div 2 = 27}$ $\mathbf{27 - 11 = 16}$ **They chose 15, 16 and 17**

Version 3

• Tell your audience to write down six consecutive numbers under 35.	20, 21, 22, 23, 24, 25
• Then tell them to add their numbers up.	$20 + 21 + 22 + 23 + 24 + 25 = 135$
• Next ask someone in the audience to shout out a multiple of 6 under 100.	84
• **Secret Step: Divide this number by 6 in your head and remember the value you get.**	$\mathbf{84 \div 6 = 14}$
• Then tell your audience to add the called out number to their total.	$135 + 84 = 219$
• Next tell them to add 3.	$219 + 3 = 222$
• Finally, tell them to multiply their answer by 17.	$222 \times 17 = 3774$
• Ask individual members of the audience for the last two digits of their answer.	74
• **Secret Step: Divide the result they give you by 2 and then subtract the number you remembered earlier. This will be the 4th value of the six consecutive numbers chosen. Reveal the six numbers chosen.**	$\mathbf{74 \div 2 = 37}$ $\mathbf{37 - 14 = 23}$ **They chose 20, 21, 22, 23, 24 and 25**

Version 4

- Tell your audience to write down seven consecutive numbers under 80.

- Then tell them to add their numbers up.

- Next ask someone in the audience to shout out a multiple of 7 under 100.
- **Secret Step: Divide this number by 7 in your head and remember the value you get.**

- Then tell your audience to add the called out number to their total.

- Finally, tell them to multiply their answer by 43.

- Ask individual members of the audience for the last two digits of their answer.

- **Secret Step: Subtract the number you remembered earlier from the answer you are given. This will be the middle value of the seven consecutive numbers chosen. Reveal the seven numbers chosen.**

44, 45, 46, 47, 48, 49, 50

$$44 + 45 + 46 + 47 + 48 + 49 + 50 = 329$$
56

$$56 \div 7 = 8$$

$$329 + 56 = 385$$

$$385 \times 43 = 16555$$

55

$$55 - 8 = 47$$

They chose 44, 45, 46, 47, 48, 49 and 50

49

Number Trick C7

Split

For this trick you need a pile of 20 or so matchsticks or coins. It is quite a complicated one to explain so you may wish to demonstrate some of the steps before trying to perform it. It will be an advantage to you if you know the squares of the numbers up to 20 when you try to interpret the result.

- Ask for a volunteer and tell them to select some matchsticks from the pile and to discard the rest.

  take 9 matchsticks

- Then ask them to split their pile into two smaller piles.

  9 split into 6 and 3

- Next tell them to multiply the numbers of matches in their two piles together and write their answer on a piece of paper.

  $6 \times 3 = 18$

- Then tell them they should repeat the process of splitting piles, multiplying the values in the two smaller piles formed and writing their answer on the same piece of paper until no further splits are possible as each pile now contains only one matchstick.

$$
\begin{array}{ccccc}
 & & 9 & & \\
 & 6 & & 3 & \\
 4 & & 2 \quad 1 & & 2 \\
2 & 2 & 1 \quad 1 & & 1 \quad 1 \\
1 \quad 1 & 1 \quad 1 & & & \\
\end{array}
$$

$4 \times 2 = 8,\ 1 \times 2 = 2$
$2 \times 2 = 4,\ 1 \times 1 = 1,\ 1 \times 1 = 1$
$1 \times 1 = 1,\ 1 \times 1 = 1$

- Finally, tell them to add up the values on the piece of paper.

  $18 + 8 + 2 + 4 + 1 + 1 + 1 + 1 = 36$

- Ask them for their answer.

  36

- **Secret Step: Multiply their answer by 2. Find the approximate square root of the result and round up. This will be the number of matchsticks they took.**

  $36 \times 2 = 72$
  $\sqrt{72} \approx 8\frac{1}{2}$
  $8\frac{1}{2} \rightarrow 9$
  They took 9 matchsticks

Number Trick C8

Three Digit Numbers

This trick is quite taxing mentally on the performer, as there are quite a few stages to the secret step you need to apply before you can reveal the numbers your volunteer chose, but it is quite an impressive one to perform. I have to admit I normally use a calculator for the final steps when I try this trick to ensure a quick and accurate prediction. I first found this trick hidden away in a brief mathematical note written by M. T. L. Bizley called "A Christmas Party Piece" in an old edition of the Mathematical Gazette (Bizley (1975)).

- Ask for a volunteer and tell them to write down a 3-digit number with all its digits different.

  275

- Then tell them to write down four more different 3-digit numbers using the same digits. (If anyone asks, <u>five</u> more different numbers are possible but you only require them to make four.)

  257, 752
  572, 527

- Next tell them to add up their five 3-digit numbers.

  $275 + 257 + 752 + 572 + 527$
  $= 2383$

- Ask them for their answer (N).

  2383

- **Secret Step: Add the digits of their answer, double this result and then find the remainder when your answer is divided by 9 (R). Then calculate 222R – N and add 1998 repeatedly to this until you get a positive answer. This is the possible arrangement of their three digits that they did not use. You can then reveal the numbers they used.**

  $2 + 3 + 8 + 3 = 16$
  $16 \times 2 = 32$
  $32 \div 9 = 3 \text{ rem } 5$
  $\therefore R = 5$
  $222 \times 5 - 2383 = -1273$
  $-1273 + 1998 = 725$
  They didn't use 725

  The five numbers used were
  257, 275, 527, 572, 752

Number Trick C9

Remainders

The three versions of the trick that I present here are simply examples of a much wider range of possibilities. Whatever numbers you want your audience to be dividing by, provided they do not share any common factors, it is possible to create a problem that uses these values. However, to do this requires some quite sophisticated mathematics. The full theory behind the trick and an indication of how to create your own tricks is explained briefly in Appendix 1. When I am actually performing these tricks, I must admit that I don't try to carry out the calculations mentally but "cheat" a little by using a calculator to speed things up.

Version 1

- Ask for a volunteer and tell them to write down a number between 1 and 60.

  47

- Then tell them to find the <u>remainder</u> that occurs when they divide their number by 3, the <u>remainder</u> that occurs when they divide their number by 4 and the <u>remainder</u> that occurs when they divide their number by 5.

  $47 \div 3 = 15$ rem 2
  $47 \div 4 = 11$ rem 3
  $47 \div 5 = 9$ rem 2

- Ask them for their three remainders <u>in order</u>.

  2, 3, 2

- **Secret Step: Calculate 40r + 45s + 36t where r, s and t are the three remainders in the order given and then subtract 60 repeatedly until you have a number in the range 1 to 60. This will be the number chosen. Then reveal their number.**

  $40 \times 2 + 45 \times 3 + 36 \times 2 =$
  287
  287 − 60 = 227
  227 − 60 = 167
  167 − 60 = 107
  107 − 60 = 47
  They chose 47

Version 2

- Ask for a volunteer and tell them to write down a number between 1 and 100.

  86

- Then tell them to find the <u>remainder</u> that occurs when they divide their number by 3, the <u>remainder</u> that occurs when they divide their number by 5 and the <u>remainder</u> that occurs when they divide their number by 7.

  $86 \div 3 = 28$ rem 2
  $86 \div 5 = 17$ rem 1
  $86 \div 7 = 12$ rem 2

- Ask them for their three remainders <u>in order</u>.

  2, 1, 2

- **Secret Step: Calculate 70r + 21s + 15t where r, s and t are the three remainders in the order given and then subtract 105 repeatedly until you have a number in the range 1 to 100. This will be the number chosen. Then reveal their number.**

  $70 \times 2 + 21 \times 1 + 15 \times 2 =$
  191
  191 − 105 = 86

  They chose 86

Version 3

- Ask for a volunteer and tell them to write down a number between 1 and 1000.
- Then tell them to find the <u>remainder</u> that occurs when they divide their number by 7, the <u>remainder</u> that occurs when they divide their number by 11 and the <u>remainder</u> that occurs when they divide their number by 13.
- Ask them for their three remainders <u>in order</u>.
- **Secret Step: Calculate 715r + 364s + 924t where r, s and t are the three remainders in the order given and then subtract 1001 repeatedly until you have a number in the range 1 to 1000. This will be the number chosen. Then reveal their number.**

812

$812 \div 7 = 116 \text{ rem } 0$
$812 \div 11 = 73 \text{ rem } 9$
$812 \div 13 = 62 \text{ rem } 6$

0, 9, 6
$715 \times 0 + 364 \times 9 + 924 \times 6$
$= 8820$
$8820 - 8 \times 1001 = 812$

They chose 812

Number Trick C10

Choices (1)

For this trick you need 24 matchsticks or other objects and three cards labelled A, B and C respectively. These cards should have the following instructions written on them:

Card A: Take as many matches as you currently have.

Card B: Take twice as many matches as you currently have.

Card C: Take four times as many matches as you currently have.

The different choices made by your volunteers will result in different numbers of matches remaining and, using your "mind reading" skill (or a little crib sheet), you will then be able to interpret how many matchsticks remain to tell the volunteers which letter each person has.

- Ask for three volunteers and give the first volunteer one match, the second volunteer two matches and the third volunteer three matches.

- Turn away and tell them each to take one of the labelled cards at random.

- Then tell them to obey the instructions on their card and take the appropriate number of matches from the remaining pile of 18 matches.

- Turn back and count the remaining matches.

- **Secret Step: To work out which volunteer took which card, consult the following table (mentally or via a crib sheet).**

1st takes B, 2nd takes C

3rd takes A

1st takes $2 \times 1 = 2$

2nd takes $4 \times 2 = 8$

3rd takes $1 \times 3 = 3$

$\therefore 18 - 2 - 8 - 3 = 5$ remain

5

Remaining matches	1st person	2nd person	3rd person
1	A	B	C
2	B	A	C
3	A	C	B
5	B	C	A
6	C	A	B
7	C	B	A

- **Reveal which person took which letter.**

1st took B, 2nd took C

3rd took A

Number Trick C11

Choices (2)

This trick is purely numerical but, as in the previous trick, relies on different combinations of remainders that link uniquely with the different choices made. I first saw this trick in an issue of the resource magazine "Mathematics Focus" produced by the Mathematics Education Team at Exeter University (CIMT (1993)).

For this trick you will need three cards numbered 0, 1 and 2 respectively and three further cards with the following numbers on:

Card A: 17, 24, 10, 38, 52
Card B: 15, 22, 43, 50, 36
Card C: 21, 35, 63, 42, 14

- Ask for three volunteers.
- Turn away and tell them each to take one of the cards labelled 0, 1 and 2 at random.
- Then tell the first volunteer to multiply the number on their card by any one of the numbers on card A.
- Next tell the second volunteer to multiply the number on their card by any one of the numbers on card B.
- Then tell the third volunteer to multiply the number on their card by any one of the numbers on card C.
- Finally, tell them to add their answers together.
- Ask them for their total.
- **Secret Step: Divide their total by 7 and find the remainder. Then consult the following table (mentally or via a crib sheet).**

1st takes 2, 2nd takes 0
3rd takes 1

$2 \times 38 = 76$

$0 \times 43 = 0$

$1 \times 35 = 35$

$76 + 0 + 35 = 111$

111

$111 \div 7 = 15$ rem 6

Remainder	1st person	2nd person	3rd person
1	0	1	2
2	0	2	1
3	1	0	2
5	1	2	0
6	2	0	1
o	2	1	0

- **Reveal which person took which number.**

**1st took 2, 2nd took 0
3rd took 1**

55

Number Trick C12

Mind Reading Cards

This is a very well known trick, so much so that it is often found as part of the collection of novelties that occur in Christmas crackers.

- Ask your audience to think of a number between 1 and 63.
- Show them the following cards and ask them to find which card or cards contains their number.

for example, if they choose 45

Card A							
1	3	5	7	9	11	13	15
17	19	21	23	25	27	29	31
33	35	37	39	41	43	45	47
49	51	53	55	57	59	61	63

A √

Card B							
2	3	6	7	10	11	14	15
18	19	22	23	26	27	30	31
34	35	38	39	42	43	46	47
50	51	54	55	58	59	62	63

B ×

Card C							
4	5	6	7	12	13	14	15
20	21	22	23	28	29	30	31
36	37	38	39	44	45	46	47
52	53	54	55	60	61	62	63

C √

Card D							
8	9	10	11	12	13	14	15
24	25	26	27	28	29	30	31
40	41	42	43	44	45	46	47
56	57	58	59	60	61	62	63

D √

Card E							
16	17	18	19	20	21	22	23
24	25	26	27	28	29	30	31
48	49	50	51	52	53	54	55
56	57	58	59	60	61	62	63

E ×

Card F							
32	33	34	35	36	37	38	39
40	41	42	43	44	45	46	47
48	49	50	51	52	53	54	55
56	57	58	59	60	61	62	63

F √

- **Secret Step: Add the first number on each card that they say their number is on. This will give the number chosen.**

$1 + 4 + 8 + 32 = 45$

56

Part D

Miscellaneous Tricks

In this, the final part of the section explaining how to perform different number tricks, I will look at some tricks that do not really fall under any of the previous three categories. Some of these tricks take a little longer to perform and the mathematics behind the tricks is often a little more involved. They are all interesting tricks in their own right and can provide opportunities for numerical discovery, algebraic proof and, most importantly, for creating a sense of wonder in your audience. As usual, each trick will be presented with a numerical example alongside to illustrate the steps in the method.

Number Trick D1

Pascal's Trick (1)

This trick is the first in a series of examples of lightning calculation, where you use a secret rule to make it appear that you have been able to carry out a set of calculations at a much greater speed than seems possible. The specifics for this particular trick were discussed in an article called "Less than 10p" by Tony Barnard that appeared in Mathematics in School (Barnard (1996)).

• Ask a volunteer to tell you any 6-digit number.	4 7 3 1 2 8
• **Secret Step: As they write down their number, look very carefully at the 2nd and 5th digits. If both are even or both are odd, write down on a piece of paper the units digit you get if you add the first and the last digits of their number. If one of the 2nd and 5th digits is odd and the other is even, write down the units digit you get if you add the first and last digits of their number to 5. This is your prediction.**	Secret step 2nd digit is 7 which is odd and 5th digit is 2 which is even. ∴ Your prediction is the units digit of $4 + 8 + 5 = 7$
• Tell them they are going to reduce their number to a 5-digit number by taking the digits in pairs (1st and 2nd, 2nd and 3rd, …), adding them and then writing down the units digit of the answer.	$4 + 7 = 11$ $7 + 3 = 10$ $3 + 1 = 4$ $1 + 2 = 3$ $2 + 8 = 10$ ∴ 5-digit number is 1 0 4 3 0
• Then tell them to continue this process until they have only one digit remaining. Remind them that they will need to be careful with their addition if the trick is going to function.	$1 + 0 = 1$ $0 + 4 = 4$ $4 + 3 = 7$ $3 + 0 = 3$ ∴ 4-digit number is 1 4 7 3 $1 + 4 = 5$ $4 + 7 = 11$ $7 + 3 = 10$ ∴ 3-digit number is 5 1 0 $5 + 1 = 6$ $1 + 0 = 1$ ∴ 2-digit number is 6 1 $6 + 1 = 7$ ∴ 1-digit number is 7
• Reveal your prediction to show that it matches the answer they have obtained.	

Number Trick D2

Pascal's Trick (2)

This trick is very similar to the previous trick, except that a larger number is used meaning the trick takes longer to perform and the rule for reducing the number of digits is altered slightly.

• Ask a volunteer to tell you any 10-digit number	2 3 0 4 8 9 6 3 4 5
• **Secret Step: As they write down their number, look very carefully at the 1st, 4th, 7th and 10th digits. Quickly calculate 1st + 10th + 3 × (4th + 7th) and then subtract 9 repeatedly until you have a number from 0 to 8. Write this value down. This is your prediction.**	$2 + 5 + 3 \times (4 + 6) = 37$ $37 - 9 - 9 - 9 - 9 = 1$ **Your prediction is 1**
• Tell them they are going to reduce their number to a 9-digit number by taking the digits in pairs (1st and 2nd, 2nd and 3rd, …), adding them and writing the answer down unless the answer is 9 or more, when they should subtract 9 and then write down that answer.	$2 + 3 = 5$ $3 + 0 = 3$ $0 + 4 = 4$ $4 + 8 = 12 \rightarrow 3$ $8 + 9 = 17 \rightarrow 8$ $9 + 6 = 15 \rightarrow 6$ $6 + 3 = 9 \rightarrow 0$ $3 + 4 = 7$ $4 + 5 = 9 \rightarrow 0$ $\therefore$ 9-digit number is 5 3 4 3 8 6 0 7 0
• Then tell them to continue this process until they have only one digit remaining. Remind them that they will need to be careful with their addition if the trick is going to function.	$5 + 3 = 8$ $3 + 4 = 7$ $4 + 3 = 7$ $3 + 8 = 11 \rightarrow 2$ $8 + 6 = 14 \rightarrow 5$ $6 + 0 = 6$ $0 + 7 = 7$ $7 + 0 = 7$ $\therefore$ 8-digit number is 8 7 7 2 5 6 7 7
	$8 + 7 = 15 \rightarrow 6$ $7 + 7 = 14 \rightarrow 5$ $7 + 2 = 9 \rightarrow 0$ $2 + 5 = 7$ $5 + 6 = 11 \rightarrow 2$ $6 + 7 = 13 \rightarrow 4$ $7 + 7 = 14 \rightarrow 5$ $\therefore$ 7-digit number is 6 5 0 7 2 4 5
	$6 + 5 = 11 \rightarrow 2$ $5 + 0 = 5$ $0 + 7 = 7$ $7 + 2 = 9 \rightarrow 0$ $2 + 4 = 6$ $4 + 5 = 9 \rightarrow 0$ $\therefore$ 6-digit number is 2 5 7 0 6 0

$2 + 5 = 7 \quad 5 + 7 = 12 \rightarrow 3$
$7 + 0 = 7 \quad 0 + 6 = 6$
$6 + 0 = 6$

∴ 5-digit number is
7 3 7 6 6

$7 + 3 = 10 \rightarrow 1$
$3 + 7 = 10 \rightarrow 1$
$7 + 6 = 13 \rightarrow 4$
$6 + 6 = 12 \rightarrow 3$

∴ 4-digit number is
1 1 4 3

$1 + 1 = 2 \quad 1 + 4 = 5$
$4 + 3 = 7$

∴ 3-digit number is
2 5 7

$2 + 5 = 7 \quad 5 + 7 = 12 \rightarrow 3$

∴ 2-digit number is
7 3

$7 + 2 = 10 \rightarrow 1$

∴ 1 digit number is
1

Reveal your prediction to show that it matches the answer they have obtained.

Number Trick D3

Faster Than A Calculator!

Most people enjoy a race, but it can be quite difficult to see how mathematics can be used within a race. In this trick, which is based on the Fibonacci sequence and is quite well known among most mathematicians, you will be able to demonstrate the speed of the mind in an addition race against a calculator. I have also included two very similar, but less well known, tricks which actually take less time to perform along with the main trick. For all these tricks, to really demonstrate your speed of thinking at the end, it will be best if you position yourself so you are unable to see the numbers written down until the race itself begins.

Version 1

- Ask for a volunteer and tell them to write down any number (although it may help to suggest that the number they use should probably be less than 10) on a board.

- Then tell them to write a 2nd number underneath the first.

- Next tell them to add their two numbers together to form a 3rd number, which they should write underneath the first two numbers.

- Then tell them they should add their 2nd and 3rd numbers to get a 4th number, then their 3rd and 4th numbers to get a 5th number and so on, adding the last two numbers in the list to get the next number until they have a list of ten numbers.

		4
		7
$4 + 7 =$		11
$7 + 11$	$=$	18
$11 + 18$	$=$	29
$18 + 29$	$=$	47
$29 + 47$	$=$	76
$47 + 76$	$=$	123
$76 + 123$	$=$	199
$123 + 199$	$=$	322

- When they have finished writing down the ten numbers in the sequence (and it would be helpful to have the rest of the audience checking their addition as they proceed so that the sequence written is formed correctly), tell them that they need their calculator as you are going to have an addition race.

- Start the race by saying "Go" and only then turn round to look at the numbers for the first time.

- **Secret Step: Multiply the 7th number in the list by 11 and announce your answer. Hopefully you will do this well before the sum is completed on the calculator!**

$$11 \times 76 = 836$$

61

Version 2

- A quicker version of the trick is to only ask for six terms of the same type of sequence to be formed.

$$
\begin{array}{c}
4 \\
7
\end{array}
$$

$$
\begin{array}{rcl}
4 + 7 & = & 11 \\
7 + 11 & = & 18 \\
11 + 18 & = & 29 \\
18 + 29 & = & 47
\end{array}
$$

- **Secret Step: Multiply the 5th number in the list by 4 (or double and then double again) to get the sum of the six terms.**

$$4 \times 29 = 116$$

Version 3

- A second variation on the trick is to have the volunteer initially write down three numbers, then form the 4th by adding the these three numbers, form the 5th number by adding the 2nd, 3rd and 4th numbers and so on, forming each new number by adding the previous three numbers until a list of eight numbers has been formed. They should then try to add this list of numbers up on a calculator while you try to beat them using only your mind.

$$
\begin{array}{c}
3 \\
5 \\
4
\end{array}
$$

$$
\begin{array}{rcl}
3 + 5 + 4 & = & 12 \\
5 + 4 + 12 & = & 21 \\
4 + 12 + 21 & = & 37 \\
12 + 21 + 37 & = & 70 \\
21 + 37 + 70 & = & 128
\end{array}
$$

- **Secret Step: Multiply the 7th number in the list by 4 to get the sum of the eight terms.**

$$4 \times 70 = 280$$

Number Trick D4

The Choice Is Yours

The next lightning addition trick is one I first saw in an American teacher resource book where it was called "Beat the Calculator" (Fraser (1984)).

- Write the following sets of 3-digit numbers on a board.
  Set A: 179 278 773 872 971 377
  Set B: 840 642 543 147 345 741
  Set C: 483 681 285 384 780 186
  Set D: 762 564 960 366 168 663
  Set E: 558 459 855 657 756 954
- Ask a volunteer to come up and, without you seeing, to choose one number from each list and to write them in a column.

  278
  147
  681
  762
  855

- Tell them that they will need a calculator as you are going to have an addition race.
- Start the race by saying "Go" and, only then, turn to look at the numbers in the column.
- **Secret Step: Add the units digits of each number. This will form the second half of your answer. Subtract this answer from 50 to get the first half of your answer.**

$8 + 7 + 1 + 2 + 5 = 23$
$50 - 23 = 27$
∴ **Full answer = 2723**

Number Trick D5 **Rectangular Adding**

The initial part of this final lightning arithmetic trick was something I saw on Kjartan Poskitt's Murderous Maths website (www.murderousmaths.co.uk), where he first uses it as a calendar trick.

For the version of the trick I will be describing, you will need a grid of numbers arranged so that the increases from one square to the next horizontally are constant and the increases from one square to the next vertically are also constant. My example will deal with a standard 100 square, but the trick will work with any square satisfying the conditions described.

- Ask a volunteer to select any 4 × 5 rectangle on the number square and to begin to add up the numbers in their rectangle. Continue to face away from the grid while explaining that you will perform the addition very quickly.
- **Secret Step: Add the number in the top left corner to the number in the bottom right corner of the rectangle and multiply by 10.**

1	2	3	4	5	6	7	8	9	10
11	12	13	14	15	16	17	18	19	20
21	22	23	24	25	26	27	28	29	30
31	32	33	34	35	36	37	38	39	40
41	42	43	44	45	46	47	48	49	50
51	52	53	54	55	56	57	58	59	60
61	62	63	64	65	66	67	68	69	70
71	72	73	74	75	76	77	78	79	80
81	82	83	84	85	86	87	88	89	90
91	92	93	94	95	96	97	98	99	100

$$(24 + 58) \times 10 = 820$$

This trick can be extended to rectangles of other sizes by using the following general rule:

Sum = ½ × (number of values in the rectangle) × (top left value + bottom right value)

or

Sum = ½ × (number of values in the rectangle) × (top right value + bottom left value)

Number Trick D6

Multiples (1)

In this quite simple trick you are going to be demonstrating your knowledge of the multiples of 11 and 13.

- Ask for a volunteer and tell them to use their calculator to work out any 4- or 5-digit multiple of 11 or 13 and then to write it down.
- Then tell them you are going to use their number to write down another, larger, multiple of 11 or 13.
- **Secret Step: Mentally split their number into two 3-digit blocks, by inserting zeros before the first figure if necessary, and then swap these blocks around.**

- Of course, you may need to add that you do not know what the expressions placed here in brackets actually are, but that was never your claim.

3 894 $(= 11 \times 354)$

or

96 889 $(= 13 \times 7453)$

You would then write

894 003

$(= 11 \times 81\,273)$

or

889 096

$(= 13 \times 68\,392)$

Number Trick D7

Multiples (2)

In this similar, but more impressive, trick, you are going to be demonstrating your knowledge of the multiples of 37.

• Ask a volunteer for any 3-digit number.	4 7 2
• Tell them you are going to use their number to write down 6- and 9-digit multiples of 37 that contain their number.	527 472
	$(= 37 \times 14\ 256)$
	472 638
	$(= 37 \times 12\ 774)$
	or
	472 615 245
	$(= 37 \times 12\ 773\ 385)$
	819 472 374
	$(= 37 \times 22\ 147\ 902)$
• **Secret Step: When you form your 6- and 9-digit numbers, mentally think of the numbers as split into groups of three digits and ensure that the digits in the corresponding positions in these groups, add to the same value.**	**e.g. in 527 472**
	5 + 4 = 9, 2 + 7 = 9,
	7 + 2 = 9
	e.g. in 472 615 245
	4 + 6 + 2 = 12,
	7 + 1 + 4 = 12,
	2 + 5 + 5 = 12

Number Trick D8

Matching Matches (1)

For this trick you will need a pile of 54 matches. I first saw this trick in an article by H. Lulli called "An Algebraic Puzzler" taken from the American teachers' journal Mathematics Teacher (Lulli (1984)).

• Place a pile of 54 matches on a table and then ask for two volunteers.	
• Tell the first to take more than 29 but fewer than 40 matches for themselves and then to give the rest to the second volunteer.	1st $\quad$ 2nd 32 $\quad\quad$ 22
• Now point out that the first volunteer has been slightly unfair and that they are going to need to return some matches.	
• Tell the first volunteer to add together the digits of the number of matches they took and to return that many matches to the second volunteer.	$3 + 2 = 5$
• Then tell them both to count how many matches they each have. They will both turn out to have the same number.	$32 - 5 = 27$ $\quad$ $22 + 5 = 27$

To vary this trick if you have different numbers of matches:

a. Using 72 matches, have the first volunteer initially take more than 39 but fewer than 50 matches.

b. Using 36 matches, have the first volunteer initially take more than 19 but fewer than 30 matches.

In each case, the two volunteers will end up with the same number of matches.

Number Trick D9

Matching Matches (2)

For this trick, you will need a large number of matches.

• Ask for three volunteers A, B and C	
• Tell A to think of a number (n)* and to tell it to B and C.	e.g. $n = 4$
• Tell A to take 4 times that number of matches from the pile.	A: $4 \times 4 = 16$
• Tell B to take 7 times that number of matches from the pile.	B: $7 \times 4 = 28$
• Tell C to take 13 times that many matches from the pile.	C: $13 \times 4 = 52$
• Now tell C to give A and B as many matches from C's pile as each of A and B currently has.	A: $16 + 16 = 32$ B: $28 + 28 = 56$ C: $52 - 16 - 28 = 8$
• Now tell B to give A and C as many matches from B's pile as each of A and C currently has.	A: $32 + 32 = 64$ C: $8 + 8 = 16$ B: $56 - 32 - 8 = 16$
• Now tell A to give C and B as many matches from A's pile as each of C and B currently has.	C: $16 + 16 = 32$ B: $16 + 16 = 32$ A: $64 - 16 - 16 = 32$
• Then tell them all to count their matches. They should each have the same number.	

* The number of matches you have originally will determine the maximum value of the number A chooses that you can allow. If you split the available matches into groups of 24 until you do not have sufficient matches to complete any more groups, then the number of complete groups is the highest value of n that volunteer A should be allowed to choose. Mathematically this is equivalent to saying that if the total number of matches T that you have satisfies

$$T = 24X + Y \qquad \text{where } 0 \leq Y \leq 23$$

then the maximum value of the number A chooses is X.

Number Trick D10

I Know How Many You Have!

For this trick as it is described, you need a large number of matchsticks. You could, however, simply draw circles on a board to represent the different groups referred to in the question and write the appropriate numbers inside the circles rather than actually dealing with objects. The original trick is taken from William Simon's book "Mathematical Magic", where he calls it "A Matchical Experiment" (Simon (1964)), whereas the variants are of my own invention.

Version 1

- Ask for a volunteer and tell them to form three equal piles of ten or more matches which we will call piles A, B and C.

A	B	C
13	13	13

- Then tell them to remove six* matches from pile A and six* matches from pile C and add all the removed matches to pile B.

13 – 6	13 + 6 + 6	13 – 6
7	25	7

- Next tell them to discard pile A.

- Then tell them to double the current size of pile C by removing the appropriate number of matches from pile B.

	25	7
	25 – 7	7 + 7
	18	14

- Next tell them to discard pile C.

18

- Finally, tell them to split pile B into two unequal parts and to give one of these parts to you.

keep 11   give away 7

- **Secret Step: Count the number of matches you are given and subtract this number from 18*. This will tell you how many matches from pile B that the volunteer has kept for themselves.**

18 – 7 = 11

- Announce how many matches from pile B that the volunteer has kept.

11 matches have been kept

*The number you subtract your matches from will always be three times the number of matches you tell the volunteer to transfer from piles A and C. Varying the number you tell your volunteer to transfer will then alter the exact details of your secret step.

Version 2

- Ask for a volunteer and tell them to form four equal piles of ten or more matches which we will call piles A, B, C and D.

A	B	C	D
16	16	16	16

- Then tell them to transfer six* matches from pile A to pile B and six* matches from pile D to pile C.

16 – 6	16 + 6	16 + 6	16 – 6
10	22	22	10

- Next tell them to combine piles B and C to make a large pile.

10	44	10

- Using matches from the large pile, tell them to double the sizes of piles A and D.

10×2	44 – 10 – 10	10×2
20	24	20

- Finally, tell them to split the large pile into two unequal parts and to give one of these parts to you. — keep 17 give away 7
- **Secret Step: Count the number of matches you are given and subtract this number from 24*. This will tell you how many matches from the large pile that the volunteer has kept for themselves.** — $24 - 7 = 17$
- Announce how many matches from the large pile that the volunteer has kept. — 17 matches have been kept

* The number you subtract your matches from will always be four times the number of matches you tell the volunteer to transfer from piles A and D. Again, varying the number you tell your volunteer to transfer will then alter the exact details of your secret step.

Version 3

- Ask for a volunteer and tell them to form four equal piles of ten or more matches which we will call piles A, B, C and D.

A	B	C	D
16	16	16	16

- Then tell them to transfer six* matches from pile A to pile B and seven* matches from pile D to pile C.

$16 - 6$	$16 + 6$	$16 + 7$	$16 - 7$
10	22	23	9

- Next tell them to combine piles B and C to make a large pile.

10	45		9

- Using matches from the large pile, tell them to double the sizes of piles A and D.

10×2	$45 - 10 - 9$	9×2
20	26	18

- Finally, tell them to split the large pile into two unequal parts and to give one of these parts to you. — keep 16 give away 10
- **Secret Step: Count the number of matches you are given and subtract this number from 26*. This will tell you how many matches from the large pile that the volunteer has kept for themselves.** — $26 - 10 = 16$
- Announce how many matches from the large pile that the volunteer has kept. — 16 matches have been kept

* The number you subtract your matches from will always be twice the sum of the numbers of matches you tell the volunteer to transfer from piles A and D.

Number Trick D11

Magic Square

Almost every book on mathematical tricks and curiosities has its section on magic squares and I see no reason why this book should be any different. However, I will not be explaining in detail that there is only one 3 × 3 square using the numbers 1 to 9 or showing how to create magic squares of different sizes. Instead the focus here will be on a magic square trick that you can actually perform.

Note: For those who are unsure, a magic square is an arrangement of numbers in a square array so that every row, every column and both diagonals of the square all add up to the same value, known as the magic constant. This is illustrated by the classic 3 × 3 square below which uses the numbers 1 to 9 and where every row, column and diagonal adds up to 15.

4	9	2
3	5	7
8	1	6

For the trick below, which deals with a 4 × 4 magic square, you will need to remember the following arrangement or at least have the arrangement written on a small piece of paper which you can keep hidden in your hand.

− 20	1	12	7
11	8	− 21	2
5	10	3	− 18
4	− 19	6	9

This is a 4 × 4 magic square with magic constant 0 and so adding any number (N) to each of the negative numbers, one of which appears in every row, column and diagonal will produce a general 4 × 4 magic square with all rows, columns and both diagonals adding up to that number.

- Tell your audience that you are going to write down a magic square.
- Start to draw the square and put in a few of the positive numbers.
- At some point, ask for a number larger than 21. This is the value you will use and will be the value of the magic constant of the square you will create.
- Complete the square by adding this value to the 4 negative numbers in your general square.
- Ask your audience to add up some rows or columns in your square. They will see that all of the rows and columns add up to the number shouted out. However, that is not all. If you ask your audience to look closely, they will see that the central 2 × 2 square and the four corner 2 × 2 squares also add up to 29.

29

9	1	12	7
11	8	8	2
5	10	3	11
4	10	6	9

Because so many of the values in the square you produce do not alter each time you create a magic square this way, your audience may get suspicious if you repeat this trick on more than one occasion. However, if you introduce a variant, then your audience will not spot what you are doing.

- Ask a volunteer to shout out a multiple of 4 above 88. Again this will be the value you use for the magic constant of the square you will create.

100

- **Secret Step: Divide this value by 4 and add the new value to <u>every</u> square in your remembered square.**

25

- When you ask your audience to check, they will see that this will give a magic square with all the rows, columns, diagonals and corner and central 2 × 2 squares adding to the number called out.

5	26	37	32
36	33	4	27
30	35	28	7
29	6	31	34

Number Trick D12

Magic Spelling

Although this trick does not deal with a classical magic square, I would say the square involved is extremely magical. I found this trick in Ian Stewart's book "The Magical Maze" (Stewart (1997)), where he credits the trick to Lee Sallows.

- Ask your audience to consider the following array of letters and numbers.

E	4	I	17	N	2	S	16
L	24	F	9	T	20	R	6
W	25	U	12	G	22	O	7
V	1	X	27	Y	11	H	3

- Tell them to choose any number from the square.
- Then tell them to spell out that number, noting the values associated with each letter.
- Next tell them to add up the numbers associated with the letters, first putting a negative sign in front of those numbers whose letter came from a shaded square.

24

T W E N T Y   F O U R
20, 25, 4, 2, 20, 11   9, 7, 12, 6

W, E, N, F and R are in
shaded squares

Sum is
$20 - 25 - 4 - 2 + 20 + 11 - 9$
$+ 7 + 12 - 6 = 24$

- They should find the answer they get is equal to the number they originally chose.

How

To Perform
The Card
Tricks

Card Tricks

A good card trick can generate lots of interest in your audience. However, unless you are prepared to put in hours of practice to learn how to manipulate the cards with false shuffles, forces or similar sleights of hand, actually carrying out the tricks can be rather difficult. That is why I like my card tricks to be simpler than this. All of the tricks in the following section will always work, provided you follow the rules carefully, because of the underlying mathematics rather than any manipulative skill. Of course you don't need to know why a trick works to be able to carry it out and indeed some of the tricks require you, as the magician, to do no maths at all. For those who are interested in the background, the mathematics behind each trick is presented separately in the second part of the book. What you do need to be able to do though is to talk to your audience and involve them in the trick, which is something that comes with practice.

I do not claim that the tricks I will describe are original. Some I have been told by different people over the years, some I have seen described in different books on magic or on the Internet and some have even featured in mathematical articles. Sometimes this makes crediting the inventor of the trick rather difficult and, while I will give the place I first found the trick and the relevant author when I know it, there will be some tricks whose provenance I do not know. In a few cases, I have devised the exact details of a particular trick myself but these are usually based on well established mathematical/magical principles and so others may well have produced the same trick previously.

For each trick, I will describe the method needed to carry out the trick, emphasising any secret steps you will need to do yourself for the trick to work. The equally important part of what to say to maintain the interest of your audience, I will leave to you. In a few cases, I have also illustrated the description with a photo of an important step of the trick to help with clarity.

Some of the tricks are similar and I have grouped these, where appropriate, together with a short introduction to the common method to save time. Unless otherwise stated, you can assume that each trick requires a full pack of cards. I hope you enjoy the tricks.

Down-Under Dealing

The first three tricks all involve a process of card elimination known in some circles as Down-Under Dealing. The aim of the process is to isolate a particular card from a packet of cards by alternately discarding one card then transferring the next card to the bottom of the packet until only one card remains. The position of the remaining card for any size packet using this method, or the very similar method that transfers the card from top to bottom first, can be determined mathematically. Eliminations of this type are closely related to a classical problem known as the Josephus Problem. This involves a group of people sitting in a circle where every X^{th} person will be eliminated until only one remains. The main interest is discovering the value of X for different values of n, the total number of people in the circle.

Card Trick 1

The 10 Card Trick

This trick can be carried out with one, two, three, four or five volunteers simultaneously.

- Ask your volunteer(s) to select ten cards at random from the pack and turn their packet face down.
- Tell them to select a number between 1 and 10.
- They should then count down their face-down packet to find the card that is in the position corresponding to their number (with 1 corresponding to the top card etc.), show that card to the rest of the audience and then return it to its original position in the packet.
- Take the packet from them and, holding the packet face-down, pretend to feel the faces of the cards with your fingers while moving cards in batches of one, two or three from the top of the packet to the bottom.
- **Secret Step: Stop after you have moved 15 cards (or 5 or 25 depending upon how much suspense you wish to create)**
- Return the packet to the volunteer and ask them if they have remembered the number they chose.
- Tell them to move that many cards, one card at a time, from the top of their face-down packet to the bottom.
- Then you are ready to find their card. This is something you can do yourself, in which case you will need to have the cards returned to you, or get them to do it themselves by following the method below.
- Alternately transfer one card from the top of the packet to the bottom and discard one card. Continue this process until you have only one card remaining in your hand. This will be the chosen card.

The trick is more impressive if you have more than one volunteer carrying out the instructions themselves as there is a greater degree of wonder that the right card has been revealed on each occasion.

Card Trick 2

Can You Find My Card?

The ideas for the next two tricks came from Martin Gardner's book "The Unexpected Hanging and Other Mathematical Diversions" (Gardner (1991)). The second trick is one he credits to an acquaintance of his, Sam Schwartz.

- Tell your audience you are thinking of a card.
- Ask someone to shout out a number from 20 to 30 (X).
- **Secret Step: Calculate $Y = 2 \times (X - 16) + 1$ and remember the Yth card dealt.**
- Ask for a volunteer to deal X cards face-up on the table.
- Announce that your card was in the pile dealt and write down the value of the card you've remembered on a piece of paper which you then put aside.
- Ask the volunteer to pick up the cards dealt, turn over the packet and then perform the following elimination method to isolate one card.
- Alternately transfer one card from the top of the packet to the bottom and discard one card. They should continue this process until they have only one card remaining in their hand.
- Reveal your written prediction and ask the volunteer to turn over the card in their hand. The values will match.

Card Trick 3

A Down-Under Trick

For this trick you need 32 cards.

- Place the pack of 32 cards on the table and ask a volunteer to take fewer than 16 cards and then to count how many cards they have.
- Pick up the rest of the pack and deal 16 cards, one at a time, into a face-up pile on the table and ask your volunteer to remember the card whose position corresponds to the number of cards they have taken.
- Discard any cards remaining in your hand.
- Turn the pile of 16 cards face-down and ask the volunteer to place the cards they have taken on top. You are now ready to find their card.
- Alternately discard one card and transfer one card from the top of the packet to the bottom. Continue this process until you have only one card remaining in your hand. This will be the chosen card.

Elimination Dealing

A second method of eliminating cards is to deal the cards into two (or more) piles, retain one pile and then continue the process until the requisite number remains. The next three tricks all utilise this process to some extent.

Card Trick 4

A Confusing Card Trick

- Ask three volunteers each to take a card from a well shuffled pack and to show it to the rest of the audience.
- Deal three piles of 14, 15 and 15 cards respectively, face-down on the table, keeping the remaining five cards in your hand.
- Tell the first volunteer to place their card face down on top of the first pile and to cover it by taking some cards (but not all cards) from the second pile.
- Tell the second volunteer to place their card face down on top of what is left of the second pile and to cover it by taking some cards (but not all cards) from the third pile.
- Tell the third volunteer to place their card face down on top of what is left of the third pile and, as no further piles remain, cover it yourself with the cards remaining in your hand.
- Gather up the cards into a single face-down pile so that the third pile is on the top, the second pile in the middle and the first pile on the bottom.
- You are now ready to find the chosen cards.
- From the top of the pile, deal the cards alternately into two smaller piles, one face-up and one face-down, starting with the face-up pile.
- Repeat the previous step with the face-down pile each time until the resulting face-down pile contains only three cards. These will be the three chosen cards.

An alternative method to the final two steps to find the chosen cards is as follows:
1. Move four cards from the bottom to the top of the pack.
2. Turn the pack face-up.
3. From the top of the pile, deal the cards alternately into two smaller piles, one face-up and one face-down, starting with the face-up pile.
4. Repeat the previous step with the face-up pile each time until the face-down pile contains only three cards. These will be the three chosen cards.

This method is not as elegant as the first as it does not keep the chosen cards out of sight until the very end and so is less impressive to perform, but it does show how variations on successful tricks can be created.

Card Trick 5

A More Confusing Card Trick

This trick is very similar in structure to the previous trick but is slightly quicker to perform and actually finds four chosen cards instead of the three found before.

- Ask four volunteers each to take a card from a well shuffled pack and to show it to the rest of the audience.
- Deal one card face-down onto a table and then three further piles of 15 cards face-down next to it going from your left to your right, keeping the remaining two cards in your hand.
- Tell the first volunteer to place their card face down on top of the single card and to cover it by taking some cards (but not all cards) from the second pile (i.e. the first pile of 15 cards).
- Tell the second volunteer to place their card face down on top of what is left of the second pile and to cover it by taking some cards (but not all cards) from the third pile.
- Tell the third volunteer to place their card face down on top of what is left of the third pile and to cover it by taking some cards (but not all cards) from the fourth pile
- Tell the fourth volunteer to place their card face down on top of what is left of the fourth pile and, as no further piles remain, cover it yourself with the two cards remaining in your hand.
- Pick up the piles from right to left so the right hand pile is on top and the left hand pile on the bottom of the face-down pack.
- Deal the cards alternately into four face-down piles.
- Choose the third pile dealt and then deal these cards alternately into four face-down piles.
- The first of these piles should contain four cards. These will be the cards chosen.

Card Trick 6

And The Missing Card Is

- Ask a volunteer to shout out a number from 1 to 20 (N).
- Deal N cards into a face-down pile.
- Deal 32 cards into a face-up pile while claiming to be memorising their positions.
- **Secret Step: Remember the N + 2nd card.**
- Turn over the face-up pile and place the remaining cards from your hand on top.
- Place this pile on top of the pile of N cards dealt earlier.
- Deal the cards alternately into two face-down piles A and B starting with pile A.
- Pick up pile B and repeat the process.
- Continue repeating the process using pile B each time until pile B contains only one card.
- Claim that you have worked out the identity of this card and tell the audience the card you remembered.
- Turn over the final card to reveal your card.

Cutting Tricks

The next few tricks all depend on the pack being cut in a particular way. Some of the cuts required are quite precise so it may be best to make sure you can cut a pack of cards accurately, or at least judge whether a pack has been cut accurately, before you try these.

Card Trick 7

A Rather Simple Trick

- Ask for a volunteer and tell them to cut the pack of cards roughly in half*.
- They should then count how many cards they have, add the digits of their answer and look at the card which lies that many cards from the bottom of their face-down pile. (For example, if they had 28 cards in their hand after cutting, they would calculate $2 + 8 = 10$ and then look at the 10th card from the bottom of their pile where the 1st card from the bottom is the bottom card itself.)
- Ask them to return the pile to you. Now spell out the phrase *a rather simple trick* dealing one card face down for each letter in the phrase.
- Once the phrase is complete, turn the next card face-up. This will be the card remembered.

*This trick will work provided the number of cards in the packet they cut is between 20 and 29 inclusive. If you think it is greater then this (i.e. between 30 and 39), then when you receive the packet, spell out *a rather simple trick to perform* and turn over the next card. This will then be the card remembered.

Card Trick 8

And One For Luck!

The next two tricks are based on ones I saw in the book "Self-Working Card Tricks" by Karl Fulves (Fulves (1976)). The first is a much altered version of his trick "The Phone Miracle" while the next follows his trick "Long Distance" more closely.

- Place a pack of cards face-down on a table.
- Ask for a volunteer and tell them to cut about a quarter of the pack*.
- Ask them to count their cards and remember that number. Then, from these cards, deal two small piles. In the first pile they should put as many cards as the first digit of their number (which should be 1) and in the second pile they should put as many cards as the second digit of their number. These cards will not be used for the remainder of the trick.
- Tell them to look at the bottom card of the remaining packet in their hand, to show it to the rest of the audience and then return the packet to you.
- Place this remaining packet face-down on top of the main pack and then, from the new pile, move the top card to the bottom – the first instance of "one for luck".
- Ask a second volunteer to shout out a number between 10 and 19. Deal this many cards, face-down from the top of the pile to form a new pile.
- Pick up the new pile and then add the digits of the number called out.
- Discard this many cards from the top of the new pile, plus one for luck, and then turn the next card face-up. This will be the card remembered.

*This trick will work provided the number of cards cut originally is between 10 and 19 inclusive.

Card Trick 9

Mind Reader

In this trick you will not touch the cards at any time but you will need a pen and paper for making notes.

- Ask for a volunteer and tell them to shuffle the cards fully and then place the pack face-down on the table.
- Tell them to cut approximately half the pack* and count how many cards they have.
- They then add together the digits of their answer and discard that many cards from the packet in their hand.
- They then mentally choose a number between 1 and 9 and discard that many cards from the remaining packet in their hand.
- With their remaining cards face-down, they then count down from the top of their packet to find the card that is in the same position as their chosen number (where a chosen number of 1 would represent the top card etc.) and show this card to the rest of the audience before replacing it in its original position.
- Then tell them that they should read out the cards in the packet in their hand one at a time from the top, making sure that they don't give away anything in their voice when it comes to their chosen card.
- **Secret Step: As they read out their cards, jot down the card values on a piece of paper. When they finish, count how many cards they have read out. Subtract this number from 18 to give you the position of the chosen card in your list.**
- After a brief pause, reveal their chosen card.

*This trick works provided the number of cards cut originally is between 20 and 29 inclusive. Occasionally, the initial packet cut will have contained 30 or more cards and so the list of cards read out to you will contain more than 18 cards. If this occurs, subtract the number of cards read out from 27 to give the position of the chosen card.

Card Trick 10   It's All In The Cut

- Ask for a volunteer and give them a well shuffled pack of cards.
- Tell them to cut the pack in half as exactly as they can* and to choose one "half" of the pack.
- Ask them to choose a card from anywhere within their pile, show it to the rest of the audience and then place it face-down on top of their pile before covering it with the other part of the pack.
- Take the pack from them and deal the cards alternately into four face-up piles.
- Ask them to indicate which pile contains their chosen card.
- Pick up the chosen pile, turn it over and deal these cards alternately into four face-down piles.
- Discard the first pile as it contains a different number of cards from the other piles.
- Pick up the remaining piles so that the middle pile is on top, the left hand pile is in the middle and the right hand pile is on the bottom of the packet in your hand.
- You are now ready to isolate their card.
- Perform the down-under deal as described in Card Tricks 2 and 3 by alternately discarding one card from the top of the packet then transferring one card from the top of the packet to the bottom. Continue this process until you have only one card remaining in your hand. This will be the chosen card.

*This is a rather sensitive trick and will only work if the part of the pack chosen contains 25, 26, 27 or 28 cards, so you may need to "help" them even out their cut before embarking on the next stages of the trick.

Spelling Tricks

The next three tricks all involve spelling out phrases or the names of your volunteers. To do this, you look to deal one card per letter (usually face-down) as you spell the appropriate words or names out loud. In Card Trick 13, the punctuation sign in the phrase is also important, so you do need to be sure you are following the rules carefully. If you try these tricks with people whose spelling is not particularly consistent, you will need to follow what they say closely as a misspelt word could mean your trick does not work.

Card Trick 11

To Lie Or Not To Lie?

For this trick you will only need a packet of nine cards.

- Deal three piles of three cards face down onto the table
- Ask a volunteer to choose a pile
- Pick up this pile and show the bottom card to the volunteer and the rest of the audience. This is their chosen card.
- Pick up the remaining piles to make a single face-down packet with the chosen pile on top.
- Tell the volunteer that you are going to ask them to spell out the chosen card or, if they prefer, to lie about which card has been chosen, either partially or totally.
- Ask the volunteer to name their card. (To illustrate the method, let us assume they say the _seven of spades._)
- Spell out the word _seven_ dealing one card per letter from the top of the face-down pile face down onto the table. Once the word is complete, place the dealt cards at the bottom of the packet.
- Repeat this process with the words _of_ and _spades_, placing the dealt cards at the bottom of the packet each time.
- Emphasise to your audience that you do not know whether they lied or told the truth so you do not know what their card is and so, if you can find it, it must be magic!
- Spell out the word _magic_, dealing one card from the top of the face-down pile for each letter apart from the final card, which you turn face-up. This will be the card remembered.

Card Trick 12

A Spelling Trick

For this trick to work, the person you choose must have a name that is more than ten letters long. I found this trick described in an article by Michael Smith in Plus magazine (Smith (1995)). It is the first of three tricks he presented over the course of a few issues in Plus and its successor Symmetry Plus that I will be examining here.

- Ask for a volunteer and tell them to remove between one and ten cards from the top of a face-down pack without showing you how many they have taken and remember how many they have removed.
- They should then count down that many cards in the remaining pack and show the card to the rest of the audience but not to you. For example, if they had removed two cards they would remember the second card in the pile.
- They then return the chosen card to its position in the pile and pass the cards to you.
- Tell them that you are going to ask them to spell out their name, dealing one card face-down for each letter and demonstrate what you mean by spelling out their full name.
- Pick up the pile of cards dealt, place them on top of the remaining cards in your hand and return the pile to them.
- Before they spell out their name, tell them to replace the cards they removed at the start of the trick on top of the pile.
- Now tell them to spell out their name, which you claim is a magic name, dealing one card face-down for each letter.
- Turn over the next card from the remaining pile. It will be the card they remembered.

Card Trick 13

The World's Greatest Magician

- Shuffle the cards fully and then place the pack face-down on a table.
- Ask a volunteer to remove fewer than 20 cards from the top of the pack and to count them, making sure you can't see how many cards they have.
- While counting out loud 1, 2, 3, … deal 20 cards from the top of the remaining pack, face-up, one at a time into a single pile asking the volunteer to remember the card whose position matches the number of cards they have removed.
- Once all 20 cards have been dealt, turn this pile over and place it at the bottom of the remaining pile.
- Ask your volunteer whether you know how many cards they removed and so whether you know which card they remembered. (Hopefully you will get the answer "no" each time!)
- Then tell them that, in that case, surely only the world's greatest magician could find their card and that you will have to ask the cards who that person is. Spell out the phrase *who is the world's greatest magician* by dealing one card per letter (not forgetting one card for the apostrophe) face down on the table.
- Turn over the next card. It will be the card remembered.

For added effect, you could create an arrow of cards pointing towards you using *who is the world's* for the shaft of the arrow and *greatest* and *magician* as the head of the arrow.

Figure 1: The arrow formed by spelling out *who is the world's greatest magician* pointing to the card that was chosen and towards you, the magician in question.

Card Trick 14

I Wish All My Card Tricks Worked This Easily

- Ask for a volunteer and tell them to think of a number between 1 and 14 inclusive.
- Give them a pack of cards and tell them to remove that many cards from the pack and keep them out of sight.
- Next tell them to look at the card that is that many from the top of the remaining face-down pack and remember it but do not move it.
- Then tell them to return the remaining pack to you.
- Deal 15 cards face-up into a pile on a table and ask your volunteer if they saw their card. They will say yes.
- Pick up this pile, turn it over and place it at the bottom of the remaining pile of cards in your hand.
- Tell your audience that the trick seems to be working very easily.
- Spell out the phrase *I wish all my card tricks worked this easily*, dealing one card per letter face-down onto the table.
- Turn over the next card. It will be the one they remembered.

Card Trick 15

A Personalised Card Trick

For this trick to work, the person you choose must have a name that is more than ten letters long.

- Ask for a volunteer and ask them to tell you their name. (To illustrate the method, let us assume their name is *Richard Johnson*.)
- Spell out the phrase *this is a Richard Johnson card trick*, dealing one card face-down onto a table for each letter in the phrase. The remaining cards can be discarded as they will not be used for the remainder of the trick.
- Gather up the cards into a single face-down pile and ask the volunteer to remove fewer than ten cards from the pile and to count them without letting you see how many cards they have.
- Then deal ten cards face-up, one at a time, into a pile on the table and ask them to remember the card whose position corresponds to the number of cards they have taken.
- Gather up these cards and replace them face-down on top of the remaining cards in your hand.
- Ask your volunteer whether you know how many cards they removed and so whether you know which card they remembered. (Hopefully you will get the answer "no" each time!)
- Then ask if they would be astonished if you could find their card. Spell out the phrase *Richard Johnson will be astonished*, dealing one card at a time, face-up into a pile on the table. (You will run out of cards at some stage before you complete the phrase. When this occurs, simply pick up the pile, turn it over and continue to deal.)
- The final card dealt will be the card remembered.

Card Trick 16
Unbelievable Mathematical Manipulation!

This trick is an example of the use of a process called Low Down Triple dealing, the basic idea of which I found in an Internet article by Colm Mulcahy with that title.

- Ask a volunteer to choose a card from the pack and to show it to the rest of the audience.
- Tell them to place it face-down on a table and then to deal a packet of between 12 and 21 cards on top, making sure that you do not see how many cards they have dealt. Any cards they have left in their hand should be discarded as they will not be required for the rest of the trick.
- Pick up their pile and tell them you are going to perform an unbelievable mathematical manipulation to make their chosen card rise from the bottom to the top of the packet.
- Spell out the word _unbelievable_ dealing one card face-down into a pile on the table for each letter.
- Place the unused cards from your hand on top and pick up the pile.
- Spell out the word _mathematical_ dealing one card face-down into a pile on the table for each letter.
- Place the unused cards from your hand on top and pick up the pile.
- Spell out the word _manipulation_ dealing one card face-down into a pile on the table for each letter.
- Place the unused cards from your hand on top and pick up the pile.
- Turn over the top card of the pile. It will be their chosen card which has magically risen to the top of the pile.

Tricks Involving Dealing Cards Into Columns

The next few tricks all involve dealing cards into different numbers of columns, gathering the cards up and then redealing into columns (and possibly repeating this process a number of times). This may sound a very simple process but unless carried out in the correct manner, you may find that the trick has not worked as you expected. With this in mind, I will briefly explain the process here to avoid repeating the explanation as part of each trick.

First, when dealing out the cards, you should deal cards face-up into columns from right to left using a face-down deck unless the trick states otherwise, dealing one card into each column before going back to the first column again. The table below gives a diagrammatic indication of the order in which you would deal the cards into three and four columns respectively. Here A represents the first card dealt, B the second card dealt and so on.

3 Columns	4 Columns
A B C	A B C D
D E F	E F G H
G H I	I J K L
etc	etc

Secondly, it is important, if the tricks are going to work correctly, that the order of cards within each column is not altered when you pick up the column. To achieve this, deal each card in a column so that it half covers the card dealt before it into that column.

Finally, when gathering up the cards, first turn the column into a single face-up pile with the first dealt card at the bottom and the other cards on top of it in the order they were dealt and then collect the piles in the necessary order.

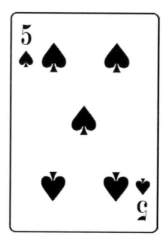

Card Trick 17

A Simple 21 Card Trick

For this trick you need 21 cards.

- Deal 21 cards into three columns of seven cards.
- Ask for a volunteer and tell them to choose a card from the ones dealt, and to indicate the column it is in.
- Gather up the columns into piles and reform the packet of 21 cards by placing the pile from the indicated column on top of another pile and then the final pile on top of that.
- Turn over the pile so it is face-down and repeat the process of dealing into three columns of seven cards and again ask the volunteer to indicate the column containing their chosen card.
- Gather up the columns into piles and reform the packet of 21 cards by placing the pile from the indicated column on top of another pile and then the final pile on top of that.
- Repeat the process of turning the pile over, dealing into three columns, having the volunteer indicate the appropriate column and gathering up the cards for a third time.
- Turn the collected cards over and spell out the magic word *Abracadabra* dealing one card face-down for each letter apart from the final card which you should turn face-up. This will be the chosen card.

Figure 2: The layout of 21 cards after one deal.

Card Trick 18

A 49 Card Trick

For this trick you need 49 cards.

- Deal the 49 cards into seven columns of seven cards.
- Ask for a volunteer and tell them to choose a card and to tell you the column their card is in.
- Pick up the cards so that the chosen column is in the centre of the pile (i.e. with three columns placed on top of it and three columns placed below it.)
- Turn the pile over and deal into seven columns of seven cards again. Ask your volunteer to tell you which column their card is in this time.
- Pick up the cards so that the chosen column is on the bottom of the pile and turn the pile over.
- Put the pile behind your back.
- **Secret Step: Transfer three cards from the top of the pile (when face-down) to the bottom and then turn the next card over so it is face-up. Cut the pack once to hide this card. Turn the pile over so the cards are face-up.**
- Spread the cards out and ask if your volunteer can see their card. They should be unable to find it but will see that one card is face-down. This will be the chosen card.

For 25 cards dealt in five columns of five, proceed in exactly the same way making sure that the first indicated column goes in the middle of the pile which will mean two columns on top of it and two columns below it. The only other difference is that in the secret step you should only move two cards from the top to the bottom of the pile before turning the next card over.

Card Trick 19

A 36 Card Trick

For this trick you need 36 cards.

- Deal the 36 cards into six columns of six cards.
- Ask for a volunteer and tell them to choose a card from the ones dealt and to tell you the column it is in. The answer you want will be in terms of the number 1, 2, 3, 4, 5 or 6 where 1 represents the column on your far left and 6 the column on your far right.
- Pick up the cards from right to left so the right hand column is on the top and subsequent piles underneath with the far left column on the bottom. Turn the packet over so that it is face-down.
- Repeat this process of dealing into six columns, asking for the number of the column containing the chosen card, gathering the cards and turning over the packet.
- **Secret Step: When they tell you the number of the column in which their card is to be found, calculate $X = A + 6 \times B - 6$ where A and B are the numbers of the columns in which the chosen card lay after one and two deals respectively.**
- Deal $X - 1$ cards face-down before turning the next card face-up. It will be the card remembered.

If you try alternate versions of this trick with 25 cards in five columns of five or 49 cards in seven columns of seven, calculate $X = A + 5B - 5$ and $X = A + 7B - 7$ respectively.

Card Trick 20

A 27 Card Trick

For this trick you need 27 cards. I first found the method for this trick and the two tricks following it in an old article by C. J. Priday (1972) in the Mathematical Gazette.

- Deal 27 cards into three columns of nine cards.
- Ask for a volunteer and tell them to choose a card from the ones dealt, then tell you the column it is in. The answer you want will be in terms of the number 1, 2 or 3 where 1 represents the column on your left, 2 the middle column and 3 represents the column on your right.
- Pick up the cards so that the left hand column is on the bottom of the packet, then the middle column with the right hand column on top. Turn the packet over so it is face down.
- Repeat this process of dealing into three columns, asking for the number of the column containing the chosen card, gathering the cards and turning over the packet on two more occasions.
- **Secret Step: When they tell you the number of the column in which their card is to be found, calculate $X = A + 3 \times B + 9 \times C - 12$ where A, B and C are the numbers of the columns in which the chosen card lay after one, two and three deals respectively.**
- Deal $X - 1$ cards face-down before turning the next card face-up. It will be the card remembered.

Card Trick 21

A Harder 21 Card Trick

This next trick is a variant on the previous trick. It is quicker to perform as fewer cards are involved, but the mental calculations you have to perform to complete it are more involved.

For this trick you need 21 cards.

- Deal 21 cards into three columns of seven cards.
- Ask for a volunteer and tell them to choose a card from the ones dealt, then tell you the column it is in. The answer you want will be in terms of the number 1, 2 or 3 where 1 represents the column on your left, 2 the middle column and 3 represents the column on your right.
- Pick up the cards so that the left hand column is on the bottom of the packet, then the middle column with the right hand column on top. Turn the packet over so it is face down.
- Repeat this process of dealing into three columns, asking for the number of the column containing the chosen card, gathering the cards and turning over the packet on two more occasions.
- **Secret Step: When they tell you the number of the column in which their card is to be found, calculate $X = A + 3 \times B + 9 \times C - 12$ where A, B and C are the numbers of the columns in which the chosen card lay after one, two and three deals respectively. Then work out $Y = X \div 4$ <u>ignoring any remainder.</u> Finally calculate $Z = X - Y$.**
- Deal $Z - 1$ cards face-down before turning the next card face-up. It will be the card remembered.

Card Trick 22

A 52 Card Trick

This trick is another variant on the previous two tricks. Again the calculations involved are more complicated than those for Card Trick 20.

- Deal 52 cards into four columns of thirteen cards.
- Ask for a volunteer and tell them to choose a card from the ones dealt, then tell you the column it is in. The answer you want will be in terms of the number 1, 2, 3 or 4 where 1 represents the column on your left, 2 the left hand of the two middle columns, 3 the right hand of the two middle columns and 4 represents the column on your right.
- Pick up the cards so that the left hand column is on the bottom of the packet, then the two middle columns with the left hand of these below the right and finishing with the right hand column on top. Turn the packet over so it is face down.
- Repeat this process of dealing into four columns, asking for the number of the column containing the chosen card, gathering the cards and turning over the packet on two more occasions.
- **Secret Step: When they tell you the number of the column in which their card is to be found, calculate $X = A + 4 \times B + 16 \times C - 20$ where A, B and C are the numbers of the columns in which the chosen card lay after one, two and three deals respectively. Then work out $Y = X \div 5$ <u>ignoring any remainder.</u> Finally calculate $Z = X - Y$.**
- Deal $Z - 1$ cards face-down before turning the next card face-up. It will be the card remembered.

Card Trick 23

A Harder 36 Card Trick

For this trick you need 36 cards. The maths you need to carry out this trick is fairly fiddly but the effect at the end is worth the effort.

- Ask for a volunteer to tell you a number between 1 and 36. (Call it N).
- **Secret Step: Subtract 1 from the number called out and then work out how many times 6 divides into your answer (A) and what remainder is left (B). (For example, if the number called out were 27, you would first calculate $27 - 1 = 26$ and then work out $26 \div 6 = 4$ remainder 2. This would mean the values of A and B you would use for the trick would be 4 and 2 respectively).**
- Deal the cards into six columns of six cards.
- Ask for a second volunteer and tell them to choose a card and to tell you the column their chosen card is in.
- Gather the columns into face-up piles and then pick up the piles one at a time and place them on top of the others so that the chosen pile has B piles underneath it. (For the example given above, the chosen pile would have two piles below it and three piles above it when you combined the piles).
- Turn the cards over so the complete packet is face-down and re-deal into six columns of six cards. Ask the volunteer to indicate in which column their card lies.
- Again gather the columns into face-up piles and then pick up the piles one at a time and place them on top of the others but this time arrange them so that the chosen pile has A piles underneath it. (For the example given above, the chosen pile would have four piles below it and one pile above it when you combined the piles).
- Turn the cards over so that the complete packet is face-down.
- Ask the first volunteer to remind you of the number they shouted out.
- Deal this many cards face-down apart from the final card which you deal face-up. This will be the card remembered.

Counting-on Tricks

The next few tricks all involve the same general idea of counting-on. To avoid repeating the details within each trick, I will explain the general method involved here.

A card is dealt face-up and its value noted. Following this, further cards are dealt on top of the face-up card, usually face-down, while counting on from the value of the face-up card until a specified total for the particular trick is reached.

For example, if the specified total for the trick is 13 and the value of the face-up card is 8, you would need to deal five extra cards on top of the face-up card by dealing one card for each of the numbers 9, 10, 11, 12 and 13 as you counted on from 8 to 13.

It is important in these tricks to take careful note of the values assigned to face cards within each trick. The two usual options are either that all of Jack, Queen and King are allocated the value 10 or that a Jack is given value 11, a Queen value 12 and a King value 13. It may also be a possibility for the specific trick that such cards cannot be used as face-up cards but instead are replaced at the bottom of the pack if they occur. Thus it is vital that the details required for the trick are noted carefully as, without following these details, the trick is unlikely to work.

Card Trick 24

A Complete Deal

- Ask for a volunteer. Instruct them to deal the cards onto a table in the following way, making sure that you can't see what they are doing.
- Tell them that in this trick, all face cards are being given the value 10.
- Then tell them to turn the top card face-up. They should then count on from its value until they reach 12 by dealing one card face-down onto the pile for each number counted.
- Once a pile is complete, they should turn the next card face-up and repeat the process.
- They then proceed in the same way until there are insufficient cards to complete the final pile.
- They should then give these remaining cards back to you and make sure the face-up cards are not visible for each pile.
- You will then turn round and, after a brief pause, tell them the total of the hidden face-up cards.
- **Secret Step: Count the spare cards when they are returned to you (C). Count the piles when you turn round (P).**
- **Then calculate $13 \times (P - 4) + C$. This is the total of the face-up cards which you can then reveal.**

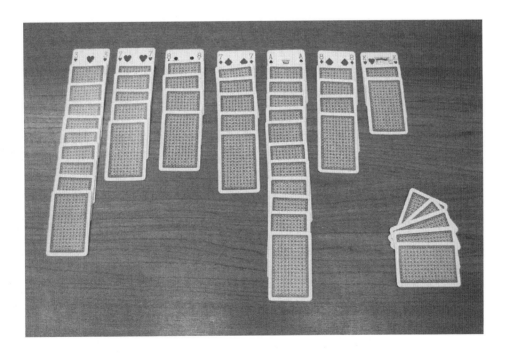

Figure 3: One possible complete deal showing the initial face-up cards, the numbers of cards dealt on each column and the spare cards. When performing this trick, you would want your volunteer to cover the face-up cards before you turn round.

Card Trick 25

Ten Is My Lucky Number

- Ask for a volunteer. Instruct them to deal the cards onto a table in the following way, making sure that you can't see what they are doing.
- Tell them that in this trick a Jack has value 11, a Queen has value 12 and a King has value 13.
- Then tell them to turn the top card face-up. They should then count on from its value until they reach 13 by dealing one card face-up onto the pile for each number counted.
- Once a pile is complete, they should turn the next card face-up and repeat the process.
- They then proceed in the same way until there are insufficient cards to complete the final pile.
- When the dealing is completed, they should turn all complete piles face down.
- They then choose any three piles at random, pick up the other piles and put them with the unused cards.
- They should then give these remaining cards back to you.
- Then they turn over the top cards of any two of these three piles.
- You then add the two values showing and deal this many cards onto the table.
- Tell the volunteer that 10 is your lucky number and then deal another ten cards onto the table. The number of cards remaining in your hand will then be equal to the value of the top card of the final pile.

If instead, four piles are chosen before the other cards are picked up and the top card of three of these piles is subsequently revealed, the value of the unrevealed top card will be equal to the number of cards left in your hand once you have dealt out four fewer cards than the sum of the three revealed values.

Card Trick 26

A Hidden Card Revealed

- Ask for a volunteer. Give them any nine cards, ask them to choose their favourite and then to show it to the rest of the audience. Then tell them to put the cards face-down on a table with their favourite card on the top.
- Put the remaining cards from the pack on top and pick up the complete pack.
- Now deal out four piles, face-up, counting down from 10 to 1, dealing one card for each number.
- If, at any time, the card dealt has the same value as the number being said, stop dealing onto that pile and move on to the next. (In this trick all face cards are taken to have value 10.)
- If this does not occur and you have counted down to 1 for a particular pile, finish that pile off by dealing an extra card, face-down, on top of that pile.
- Once you have completed all four piles, add up the values still visible (X).
- Deal X – 1 cards face-down before turning the next card face-up. This will be the card remembered.

If all the piles have a face-down card on the top, then the value of X would be 0 and the card remembered would be the face-down card dealt on the final pile.

Figure 4: For the deal illustrated, the value of X would be 4 + 10 + 5 = 19 as the 3rd column has counted down fully from 10 to 1 and has been finished off with a face-down card on top

Card Trick 27

Lucky 7

I first saw this trick explained in an article by Michael Smith in Symmetry Plus magazine (Smith (1996)).

- Ask for a volunteer and ask them to tell you a number between 1 and 19 (N).
- Discard this many cards from the top of a face-down pack.
- Deal the next 26 cards face-up into a pile on the table, claiming that you are memorising the cards.
- **Secret Step: Only memorise the N + 7th card.**
- Gather up the pile of 26 cards and add them to the bottom of the cards remaining in your hand.
- Now turn over the top three cards of the pack and find their total value (X), assuming that all face cards take the value 10.
- For each of the face-up cards, count on from that value to make the value up to 10 by dealing one card face-down on the pile for each number counted.
- Claim that you have remembered the Xth card remaining in your hand and tell the audience the card you secretly memorised.
- Deal X – 1 cards face-down on the table before turning the next card face-up. It will be the card you memorised.

Card Trick 28

Lucky 13

This trick is very similar to the previous trick. However, in this trick, the face cards do not take value 10 but instead a Jack has value 11, a Queen has value 12 and a King has value 13.

- Before starting the trick, claim to be able to memorise a sequence of cards as they are dealt.
- From a face-down pack, deal one card at a time, face-up onto a table to form a single pile. Continue dealing until you have dealt about half the pack.
- **Secret Step: At some stage, memorise a card and then deal exactly ten more cards on top of it.**
- Now ask a volunteer to choose three cards at random from the cards remaining in your hand and to place them face-up on the table.
- Turn over the pile of cards containing your memorised card and place it underneath the pile of cards still in your hand.
- For each of the face-up cards, count on from that value to make the value up to 13 by dealing one card face-down on the pile for each number counted.
- Ask someone to add up the values of the three face-up cards and to tell you the answer (X).
- Reveal that you know the value of the Xth card in your hand and that it is the card you memorised.
- Deal X – 1 cards face-down on the table before turning the next card face-up. It will be the card you memorised.

Miscellaneous Tricks

The next few tricks have little in common beyond the fact that they are mathematical in nature and require no set-up in advance. They do, however, include some of my favourite tricks and some of the ones that first got me thinking about how card tricks involving mathematics can be a valid tool for use in the classroom and beyond.

Card Trick 29

Jack!

This trick was one I first came across when it was presented by Rob Eastaway as part of a video link session with groups of children in different parts of the country, although he had some special cards made so that it was a Bart Simpson card rather than a Jack that was hiding itself.

For this trick you need only seven cards – a red Jack, three small clubs and three small spades.

- Show the cards to your audience and inform them that the Jack is very good at hiding and that when he hides, they will not be able to find him.
- Put the Jack in the middle of the cards, turn the packet so that the backs of the cards are towards your audience and start to shuffle.
- **Secret Step: Stop shuffling when the Jack is the card facing you at the front of the packet.**
- Ask your audience for a number between 2 and 6. (To illustrate the method, let us assume **4** was chosen.)
- Hold the packet up to your audience so they can only see the back of the card at the back of the packet (and you can see the Jack). Move **four** cards from the back of the packet to the front, one card at a time. As you move the **fourth** card, turn it over so that is facing the audience to show that it is not the Jack before placing it at the front of the packet.
- Repeat this process until all the cards except one are facing the audience.
- The one card that has not been turned over will be the Jack.

This trick will work using any prime number of cards (p), provided that Jack is initially closest to you and the number chosen is between 2 and p – 1.

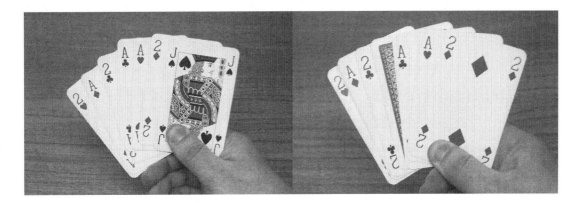

Figure 5: a) The initial position of the Jack from the point of view of the magician.
b) The final positioning of the cards from the point of view of the observer if the number chosen was 4.

Card Trick 30

Double Dealing

This trick is taken from "Self-Working Card Tricks" by Karl Fulves (Fulves (1976)), where he calls it "Child's Play".

- Ask for a volunteer and tell them to deal two equal piles of cards face-down onto the table, making sure they count how many cards are in each pile.
- Tell the volunteer to pick up one of the piles and look at the bottom card before putting the pile back face-down on the table.
- Ask a second volunteer to cut some cards from the second pile, look at the bottom card of the cards they have taken and then put this packet on top of the first pile before placing this larger pile on top of the remainder of the second pile.
- You now pick up the combined pile and point out that as you do not know how many cards the second volunteer selected, you are not aware of where the chosen cards are.
- Ask the first volunteer to tell you how many cards were dealt into each pile (X).
- Deal X cards from the top of the combined pile face-down onto the table and then turn the remaining cards face-up and place this pile next to the face-down pile.
- Ask your two volunteers to tell you to stop if they see their card being dealt.
- Now deal cards simultaneously from the top of each pile until one of your volunteers sees their card being dealt from the top of the face-up pile and tells you to stop.
- Reveal the card being dealt at the same time from the top of the face-down pile. It will be the other volunteer's chosen card.

Card Trick 31

Four Into Three Does Go!

The only place I have ever seen this trick described was in an article called "Some Variations on a Mathematical Card Trick" by L. M. Markovitz from the American teachers' journal, Mathematics Teacher (Markovitz (1983)).

- Ask a volunteer to choose a card from a well shuffled pack.
- Now tell your audience that you are going to start to deal the remaining cards face down into four equal piles until someone tells you to stop. (Note: the piles must all have the same number of cards when you stop.)
- Discard any unused cards.
- Tell the volunteer to place their card on top of any one of the piles and to hide it by placing any other pile on top.
- Pick up the piles by placing one remaining pile on top of the large pile and the final pile underneath the larger pile.
- Start to deal the cards into three face-down piles, noting carefully where the final card falls.
- **Secret Step: If the final card is dealt onto the first pile, retain that pile. If the final card is dealt onto the second pile, retain the third pile. If the final card is dealt onto the third pile, retain the second pile.**
- Repeat this process of dealing into three piles using the pile of cards you retained from the previous deal, until the chosen pile contains only one card. This will be the chosen card.

Card Trick 32

Talking Cards

For this trick you need a full pack of cards plus two extra Queens which have a different design on the back.

- Place the full pack of cards face-down on the table.
- Take the two extra Queens and insert them into the pack so they are the 10th and 29th cards from the top.
- Ask a volunteer to come and cut about a third of the pack, show the bottom card to the rest of the audience and then place their pile face down on the table (Pile 1).
- Ask a second volunteer to come and cut about half the remaining pack, show the bottom card to the rest of the audience and then place their pile face-down on the table (Pile 2).
- Rebuild the pack by placing Pile 2 on top of Pile 1 and this combined pile on top of the remaining cards.
- Keeping the cards face-down, look through the pack for the two Queens.
- As you find the Queens, remove them and break the pack into three face-down piles: Pile A (above the first Queen), Pile B (between the Queens) and Pile C (below the second Queen).
- Rebuild the pack without the two Queens by placing Pile A on top of Pile C and the combined pile on top of Pile B.
- Pretend to talk to the Queens before revealing that they have told you that the chosen cards are the 18th and 43rd cards in the pack.
- Deal 17 cards face-down before turning over the 18th card. Deal a further 24 cards face-down before turning over the 43rd card. They will be the two cards chosen.

This trick will work provided the first cut is between the two Queens and the second cut is below the second Queen. Different initial positions for the two Queens lead to different final positions of the chosen cards. This is explained in the mathematical section in the second half of the book.

Card Trick 33

I'll Feel It In My Fingers!

- Ask for a volunteer from the audience and tell them to take between 1 and 20 cards from the top of the pack, to count them without you seeing and then to let the rest of the audience know how many cards they have.
- While counting out loud 1, 2, 3, … deal 20 cards from the top of the remaining pack, face-up, one at a time into a single pile asking the volunteer to remember the card whose position matches the number of cards they have removed.
- Turn this pile face-down and set it aside.
- Ask a second volunteer to shout out a number that is smaller than the number of cards still in your hand. (Call it N.)
- Deal this many cards face-down onto the table, put the packet of 20 cards set aside earlier on top and any remaining cards in your hand on top of these.
- Ask your audience to think clearly about the card remembered, telling them that the face of the card they chose will become hot so you will be able to feel the right card.
- From the top of the face-down pack, transfer one card at a time from your left hand to your right whilse pretending to feel the face of the card.
- **Secret Step: While transferring and feeling the cards, silently count from 20+N+1 up to 52.**
- The final card moved will be the one remembered.

Card Trick 34

Third Time Lucky

This trick was described in Martin Gardner's seminal work on mathematical magic "Mathematics, Magic and Mystery" (Gardner (1956)), where he calls it "The Keystone Card Discovery" and credits its invention to Charles T Jordan in 1920.

- Take a pack of cards and glance through them.
- **Secret Step: Remember the top card of the face-down pack.**
- Place the pack face down on a table and tell your audience that you can predict the card they are going to choose.
- State the name of the card you remembered earlier.
- Tell your audience that you are going to test the theory "Third Time Lucky".
- Ask a volunteer for a number below 20.
- Deal this many cards face-down onto the table and then turn over the top card of the remaining pack, stating confidently that this will be your predicted card.
- Unfortunately, this will be incorrect and so replace the turned over card on top of the pack, pick up the cards dealt and put these back on top of the revealed card.
- Tell your audience that the number they chose must have been too small and ask a second volunteer for a number between 20 and 40 inclusive.
- Deal this many cards face-down onto the table and then turn over the top card of the remaining pack, again stating confidently that this will be your predicted card.
- Unfortunately, this will be incorrect once again and so replace the turned over card on top of the pack, pick up the cards dealt and put these back on top of the revealed card.
- Point out that you have been unlucky twice so far so but if the theory of "Third Time Lucky" holds, you will be right if you try one more time.
- Ask what the difference between the two numbers called out was.
- Deal this many cards face-down onto the table and then turn over the top card of the remaining pack, stating now more with hope than expectation, that this will be your predicted card.
- Despite any misgivings, this will be the predicted card, thus demonstrating that the theory of "Third Time Lucky" does indeed hold.

Card Trick 35

Reading Minds

- Ask for a volunteer and tell them to think of a number from 1 to 20 inclusive.
- Tell them you are going to deal between 20 and 30 cards face-up onto the table and that they should tell you when they want you to stop dealing. Also tell them to remember the card in the same position as their number.
- **Secret Step: You need to keep a careful count of how many cards you deal at this stage (Y). Work out C = 52 – Y and remember this number.**
- Give the remaining pack to the volunteer and turn your back.
- Tell them to deal cards from the top of the remaining pack face-down onto the table until they have dealt as many as the original number they thought of.
- Next tell them to turn the face-up pile over, place it on top of the pile they have just dealt and put any remaining cards in their hand on top of that.
- Turn back and ask for the pack. Tell the volunteer you are going to deal cards face-up onto the table and that you are going to read their mind to decide when their card has appeared.
- Deal cards face-up onto the table until you have dealt out the number (C) you remembered earlier. The last card will be the one chosen.

Card Trick 36

Mental Agility

The next two tricks do involve moving some cards around without your audience being aware of what you are doing and so may take some practice before they can be performed smoothly but they do still fall into the category of mathematical tricks. The majority of the methods for both tricks come from the tricks on the website www.card-trick.com which has pages of card tricks for the budding magician to perform, both of the mathematical self-working type considered within this book and those that require more skilful card manipulation and sleight of hand.

- Ask for a volunteer and tell them to think of a number between 1 and 10 inclusive.
- Give them a pack of cards and tell them to find the card that is that many from the top of the face-down pack and remember it but not to move it.
- Then tell them to return the pack to you.
- **Secret Step: Put the pack behind your back and count off 19 cards from the top of the pack reversing their order as you go. Then replace these 19 cards on the top of the pack.**
- Return the pack to your volunteer and announce that you have put their card at position 20 in the pack.
- Ask them for their number and tell them to start counting on from their number, dealing one card at a time face-down.
- When they reach 20, tell them to turn that card over. It will be the card they remembered.

Variation

- Ask for an initial volunteer and tell them to shout out a number from 15 to 20 inclusive (X).
- Proceed as before but change the number of cards moved during the secret step to one fewer than the number called out (X – 1).
- When your volunteer is dealing out cards at the end of the trick, their card will appear at the position of the number shouted out.

Card Trick 37

A Cool Card Trick

- Ask for a volunteer and tell them to choose a card at random from the pack and to place it face-down on the table.
- Then ask for a second volunteer and tell them to think of a number from 1 to 10 inclusive.
- Turn your back and tell the second volunteer to deal out two piles of cards, each containing that number of cards.
- Next tell them to put one pile in their pocket and to place the other pile on top of the first volunteer's card.
- Then tell them to place that pile, including the first volunteer's card, on top of the remainder of the pack.
- Turn back to face the volunteers and ask for the pack of cards.
- **Secret Step: Count off a packet of 15 cards, reversing the order of the cards as you do it, and then place this packet back on top of the pack.**
- Ask the second volunteer to return the packet of cards from their pocket to the top of the pack.
- Spell out the phrase *A Cool Card Trick*, dealing one card face-down from the top of the pack each time.
- Turn over the next card. It will be the one chosen by the first volunteer.

If you change the size of the packet of cards you count off during the secret step (from 15 to Y), you will change the final position of the chosen card (to the Yth). This means that you can use any phrase you want to reveal the card, provided the phrase is one letter smaller than the number of cards you reverse and that you reverse more than 10 cards to be certain that the chosen card has been moved.

Set-up Tricks

All of the tricks I have described so far have worked with packs of cards that require no set-up in advance. The next four tricks in the section do require a small packet of cards to be arranged in advance, but they are quite nice tricks to perform and so I have included them here.

Card Trick 38

The Ten Card Line

For this trick you need cards with values 1 to 10 in order. It is best if you do not actually tell your audience that this is what you have as the trick is slightly spoilt otherwise.

- Deal the cards face-down in a line so that the 10 is on the right and the Ace is on the left.
- Ask for a volunteer and tell them you are going to ask them to move some number of cards between 1 and 9 from the left hand end to the right hand end, one card at a time.
- Demonstrate what you mean by moving two cards.
- Turn away and allow them to carry out their moves unobserved.
- When they have finished, turn over the third card from the right hand end.
- The value on the card will be the number of cards moved.

The trick can be repeated from the position left by the first move without resetting the line (although you no longer need to demonstrate the structure of the move). On this occasion you will turn over the Xth card from the right where $X = 3 +$ number of cards moved on the first occasion.

If you ever turn over the 10, then your instructions have not been followed and either 0 or 10 cards have been moved.

Card Trick 39

Magic Spelling

For this trick you need the cards of one suit arranged in the following order from the top of a face-down packet: 3, 8, 7, A, Q, 6, 4, 2, J, K, 10, 9, 5.

- Briefly show the packet of cards to your audience claiming that the cards are in a random order but that by magic, you will be able to make each card appear on cue. (Of course, your claim of a random order is totally untrue!)
- Turn the packet face-down and spell out the first value A, C, E moving one card per letter from the top of the packet to the bottom.
- Turn over the next card revealing the Ace and place it on a table.
- Spell out the next value T, W, O, again moving one card per letter from the top to the bottom of the packet before turning the next card over to reveal the 2. Place this card on top of the Ace.
- Repeat this process, revealing the desired card each time, until you have only one card in your hand. It will be the King.

If you want to vary this trick slightly, you can reveal the card as you say the final letter of its value. This requires the initial order of the cards to be different from above. The packet should now be arranged as Q, 4, A, 8, K, 2, 7, 5, 10, J, 3, 6, 9.

Card Trick 40

Stop!

For this trick you need a face-down packet consisting of cards numbered 1 to 9 in order, with the 9 on the bottom of the packet. You will also need the rest of the pack.

- Cut the packet once so that the 6 is now on the bottom. (i.e. move the bottom three cards to the top of the packet.)
- Now tell a volunteer that you are going to move one card at a time from the top of the face-down packet to the rest of the pack until told to stop
- Start moving one card at a time but do not move the card you are holding or just about to move when told to stop. This is your prediction card.
- Ask the volunteer to cut the pile formed by the rest of the pack and the cards you have already moved into two or more piles.
- They should then count the cards in each pile and find the sum of the digits of each answer.
- They then add these digit sums together and find the digit sum of this answer, repeating the process until a single figure answer is obtained.
- Reveal the value of the stop card. This will be the answer they obtained.

To illustrate this process, suppose six cards were moved to the remaining pile (the 7, 8, 9, A, 2 and 3 from your packet) and the resulting pile of cards was cut into piles of 16 and 33 cards respectively.

The digit sums of the answers would be $1 + 6 = 7$ and $3 + 3 = 6$

The sum of these digit sums would be $6 + 7 = 13$

This would reduce to $1 + 3 = 4$

which would be the card at the top of the remaining packet.

Card Trick 41

Skilful Shuffling

This trick and its variants are based on the mathematical result known as the Gilbreath principle after the mathematician and amateur magician Norman Gilbreath who discovered it in 1958 (Gardner 1985). It does require the pack of cards to be set up beforehand but, when performed, the effect is quite surprising.

- Arrange the pack of cards so that the colours of the cards alternate.
- Deal about half the pack face down onto the table.
- Perform a riffle shuffle to join the two parts of the pack.
- Ask your audience to guess whether successive pairs of cards will be the same colour or different colours.
- Deal pairs of cards from the top of the pack. Every pair will consist of one black and one red card.

Variant 1

- Arrange the pack in 13 groups of four cards so that the suits of the cards form a repeating sequence (eg Hearts, Clubs, Spades, Diamonds, Hearts, Clubs, …).
- Repeat the process described above of dealing roughly half the pack face down onto the table and then riffle shuffling the two parts together.
- Deal cards in groups of four from the top of the pack. Every group of four cards will contain one card of each suit.

Variant 2

- Arrange the pack in four groups of 13 cards so that the cards in each group are in the same numerical order.
- Repeat the process described above of dealing roughly half the pack face down onto the table and then riffle shuffling the two parts together.
- Deal cards in groups of 13 from the top of the pack. Every group of 13 cards will contain one card of each value.

Variant 3

- Arrange the pack of cards so that the conditions described in all three examples are satisfied (eg AH, 2C, 3D, 4S, 5H, 6C, 7D, 8S, 9H, 10C, JD, QS, KH, AC, 2D, etc).
- Repeat the process described above of dealing roughly half of the pack face down onto the table and then riffle shuffling the two parts together.
- Every pair of cards from the top will be different colours, every group of four cards from the top will contain cards of the four different suits and every group of 13 cards from the top will contain one card of each value.

Card Trick 42

You Do As I Do

This final trick, which is another one I found somewhere on the Internet, is totally different from all the other tricks in as much as there is no mathematics of any kind in its structure. I have included it here, because it is both a nice trick to perform and it is an example of a different type of trick, known as a key card trick, that any budding magician without skills in sleight of hand can still learn to perform. The key to the trick is that you know the value of a particular card in a particular position at some point during the trick and are able to use this information to work out a card chosen by someone else.

For this trick you need two full packs of cards.

- Ask for a volunteer and tell them to take one pack of cards and shuffle it well while you do the same to the other pack. Tell them you are going to try and copy their actions as closely as you can so you can obtain similar results.
- **Secret Step: As you finish shuffling, make sure you see the bottom card of your pack and remember it.**
- Swap packs and then ask your volunteer to choose a card from the centre of the pack while you do the same from your pack.
- Tell them to place their chosen card on the top of their face-down pack and to cut the pack a couple of times to hide the card while you, again, do the same to your pack.
- Swap packs again and tell them to try and find the card they chose within the pack while you do the same.
- **Secret Step: Look for the card you memorised earlier. The card you then choose is the one directly underneath that one when the pack is face-down.**
- Tell the volunteer to place their card face-down on a table while you do the same.
- Tell the audience that, as you both did exactly the same thing, you both should have chosen exactly the same card. Hopefully they will not believe you, but when you both turn over your cards, they will indeed be the same.

Why

The Number
Tricks
Work

Part A

And Your Answer Is

Number Trick A1

Think Of A Number (1)

In each of the versions considered in this trick, the proof involves the manipulation and eventual elimination of the unknown number chosen. In each case, I will call the number chosen X (to avoid confusion with the multiplication sign) and track the operations that are applied to the number. This notation will also be applied to all similar one value tricks in this and the other number trick sections.

Version 1

$$X \rightarrow 2X \rightarrow 2X + 10 \rightarrow (2X + 10) \div 2 = X + 5 \rightarrow 5$$

Version 2

$$X \rightarrow 2X \rightarrow 2X + 6 \rightarrow 2(2X + 6) = 4X + 12 \rightarrow 4X + 16 \rightarrow (4X + 16) \div 4 = X + 4 \rightarrow 4$$

Version 3

$$X \rightarrow 3X \rightarrow 3X + 6 \rightarrow 4(3X + 6) = 12X + 24 \rightarrow 12X + 32 \rightarrow (12X + 32) \div 2 = 6X + 16 \rightarrow 6X + 12 \rightarrow (6X + 12) \div 6 = X + 2 \rightarrow 2$$

Number Trick A2

Think Of A Number (2)

The methods of proof for the versions of this trick are very similar to those used for the previous trick, although some of the algebra does get a little more involved as it requires algebraic expressions to be factorised.

Version 1

$$X \rightarrow X^2 \rightarrow X^2 - 4 \rightarrow (X^2 - 4) \div (X - 2) = (X + 2) \times (X - 2) \div (X - 2) = X + 2 \rightarrow 2$$

(The factorisation of $X^2 - 4$ into $(X + 2) \times (X - 2)$ that is used here is known as the difference of two squares.)

Version 2

$$X \rightarrow X \times (X + 4) = X^2 + 4X \rightarrow X^2 + 4X + 4 = (X + 2)^2 \rightarrow \sqrt{(X + 2)^2} = X + 2 \rightarrow 2$$

If the original number is negative ($X = -A$ where A is positive) then the negative square root must be used and the sequence of calculations works as follows:
$$-A \rightarrow -A \times (-A + 4) = A^2 - 4A \rightarrow A^2 - 4A + 4 = (A - 2)^2 \rightarrow -\sqrt{(A - 2)^2} = -(A - 2)$$
$$= -A + 2 \rightarrow -A + 2 -(-A) = 2$$

Version 3

$$X \rightarrow 4X \rightarrow 4X \times (X + 1) = 4X^2 + 4X \rightarrow 4X^2 + 4X + 1 = (2X + 1)^2$$
$$\rightarrow \sqrt{(2X + 1)^2} = 2X + 1 \rightarrow 2X \rightarrow 2X \div X = 2$$

In a similar way to version 2, if the original number is negative ($X = -A$ where A is positive) then the negative square root must be used and the sequence of calculations works as follows:
$$-A \rightarrow -4A \rightarrow -4A \times (-A + 1) = 4A^2 - 4A \rightarrow 4A^2 - 4A + 1 = (2A - 1)^2$$
$$\rightarrow -\sqrt{(2A - 1)^2} = -(2A - 1) = -2A + 1 \rightarrow -2A \rightarrow -2A \div (-A) = 2$$

Version 4

$$X \rightarrow X^3 \rightarrow X^3 - 8 \rightarrow \mathbf{(X^3 - 8) \div (X - 2) = X^2 + 2X + 4} \rightarrow X^2 + 3X + 4$$
$$\rightarrow X^2 + 4X + 4 = (X + 2)^2 \rightarrow \sqrt{(X + 2)^2} = X + 2 \rightarrow 2$$

The step highlighted in bold print is more advanced and requires the algebraic factorisation of $X^3 - 8$ into $(X - 2) \times (X^2 + 2X + 4)$ before the division can take place.

Version 5

$$X \rightarrow X \times (X - 1) = X^2 - X \rightarrow (X^2 - X) \times (X + 1) = X^3 - X \rightarrow X^3 \rightarrow 8 X^3$$
$$\rightarrow \sqrt[3]{(8 X^3)} = 2X \rightarrow 2X \div X = 2$$

Version 6

$X \rightarrow 2X \rightarrow (2X)^2 = 4X^2 \rightarrow 4X^2 \times (4X^2 + 2) = 16X^4 + 8X^2 \rightarrow 16X^4 + 8X^2 + 1$
$= (4X^2 + 1)^2 \rightarrow \sqrt{((4X^2 + 1)^2)} = 4X^2 + 1 \rightarrow 4X^2 \rightarrow \sqrt{(4X^2)} = 2X \rightarrow 2X \div X = 2$

Number Trick A3

Palindromic Puzzles

Before starting the individual proofs of these tricks, note the fact that the number ab formed using the two digits a and b is equivalent to $10a + b$ and the number abc formed using the three digits a, b and b is equivalent to $100a + 10b + c$ etc.

Version 1

Let the number chosen be aba $= 100a + 10b + a$

Because of the restriction given in the set-up of the trick, $a + b = 7$
∴ the number chosen is $100a + 10 \times (7 - a) + a = 91a + 70$
$(91a + 70) \div 7 = 13a + 10$
$(13a + 10) \div 13 = a$ remainder 10

Version 2

Let the number chosen be aba $= 100a + 10b + a$

Because of the restriction given in the set-up of the trick, $a + b = 14$
∴ the number chosen is $100a + 10 \times (14 - a) + a = 91a + 140$
$(91a + 140) \div 7 = 13a + 20$
$(13a + 20) \div 13 = (a + 1)$ remainder 7

Version 3

Let the number chosen be aba $= 100a + 10b + a$

Because of the restriction given in the set-up of the trick, $a + b = 13$
∴ the number chosen is $100a + 10 \times (13 - a) + a = 91a + 130$
$(91a + 130) \div 13 = 7a + 10$
$(7a + 10) \div 7 = (a + 1)$ remainder 3

Version 4

Let the number chosen be abba $= 1000a + 100b + 10b + a$

Because of the restriction given in the set-up of the trick, $a + b = 9$
∴ the number chosen is $1000a + 100 \times (9 - a) + 10 \times (9 - a) + a = 891a + 990$
$(891a + 990) \div 11 = 81a + 90$
$(81a + 90) \div 9 = 9a + 10$
$(9a + 10) \div 3 = (3a + 3)$ remainder 1

Number Trick A4

All The Twos

Version 1

Let the three digits chosen be a, b and c

∴ the six 2-digit numbers formed are equal to $10a + b$, $10a + c$, $10b + a$, $10b + c$, $10c + a$, $10c + b$

∴ the sum of the six 2-digit numbers is
$10a + b + 10a + c + 10b + a + 10b + c + 10c + a + 10c + b = 22a + 22b + 22c$

Dividing by the sum of the original three digits gives
$22a + 22b + 22c \div (a + b + c) = 22(a + b + c) \div (a + b + c) = 22.$

Version 2

Let the four digits chosen be a, b, c and d

∴ the 12 2-digit numbers formed are equal to $10a + b$, $10a + c$, $10a + d$, $10b + a$, $10b + c$, $10b + d$, $10c + a$, $10c + b$, $10c + d$, $10d + a$, $10d + b$, $10c + d$

∴ the sum of the 12 2-digit numbers is
$10a + b + 10a + c + 10a + d + 10b + a + 10b + c + 10b + d + 10c + a + 10c + b + 10c + d + 10d + a + 10d + b + 10c + d = 33a + 33b + 33c + 33d$

Dividing by the sum of the original four digits gives
$33a + 33b + 33c + 33d \div (a + b + c + d)$
$= 33(a + b + c + d) \div (a + b + c + d) = 33$

Version 3

Let the three digits chosen be a, b and c

∴ the six 3-digit numbers formed are equal to $100a + 10b + c$, $100a + 10c + b$, $100b + 10a + c$, $100b + 10c + a$, $100c + 10a + b$, $100c + 10b + a$

∴ the sum of the six 3-digit numbers is
$100a + 10b + c + 100a + 10c + b + 100b + 10a + c + 100b + 10c + a + 100c + 10a + b + 100c + 10b + a = 222a + 222b + 222c$

Dividing by the sum of the original three digits gives
$222a + 222b + 222c \div (a + b + c) = 222(a + b + c) \div (a + b + c) = 222$

Version 4

Let the four digits chosen be a, b, c and d

∴ the 24 3-digit numbers formed are equal to

100a + 10b + c, 100a + 10b + d, 100a + 10c + b, 100a + 10c + d, 100a + 10d + b,
100a + 10d + c, 100b + 10a + c, 100b + 10a + d, 100b + 10c + a, 100b + 10c + d,
100b + 10d + a, 100b + 10d + c, 100c + 10a + b, 100c + 10a + d, 100c + 10b + a,
100c + 10b + d, 100c + 10d + a, 100c + 10d + b, 100d + 10a + b, 100d + 10a + c,
100d + 10b + a, 100d + 10b + c, 100d + 10c + a, 100d + 10c + b

∴ the sum of the 24 3-digit numbers is

100a + 10b + c + 100a + 10b + d + 100a + 10c + b + 100a + 10c + d + 100a + 10d + b
+ 100a + 10d + c + 100b + 10a + c + 100b + 10a + d + 100b + 10c + a + 100b + 10c +
d + 100b + 10d + a + 100b + 10d + c + 100c + 10a + b + 100c + 10a + d + 100c + 10b
+ a + 100c + 10b + d + 100c + 10d + a + 100c + 10d + b + 100d + 10a + b + 100d +
10a + c + 100d + 10b + a + 100d + 10b + c + 100d + 10c + a + 100d + 10c + b

$$= 666a + 666b + 666c + 666d$$

Dividing by the sum of the original four digits gives

$$666a + 666b + 666c + 666d \div (a + b + c + d)$$
$$= 666(a + b + c + d) \div (a + b + c + d) = 666$$

Version 5

Let the three 2-digit numbers chosen be ab, cd and ef (equivalent to $10a + b$, $10c + d$, $10e + f$)

∴ the six 4-digit numbers formed are equal to

100(10a + b) + 10c + d, 100(10a + b) + 10e + f, 100(10c + d) + 10a + b,
100(10c + d) + 10e + f, 100(10e + f) + 10a + b, 100(10e + f) + 10c + d

∴ the sum of the six 4-digit numbers is

100(10a + b) + 10c + d + 100(10a + b) + 10e + f + 100(10c + d) + 10a + b +
100(10c + d) + 10e + f + 100(10e + f) + 10a + b + 100(10e + f) + 10c + d

$$= 2020a + 202b + 2020c + 202d + 2020e + 202f$$

Dividing by the sum of the original three 2-digit numbers gives

$$2020a + 202b + 2020c + 202d + 2020e + 202f \div (10a + b + 10c + d + 10e + f)$$
$$= 202(10a + b + 10c + d + 10e + f) \div (10a + b + 10c + d + 10e + f) = 202$$

Number Trick A5

1089 And All That

Let the 3-digit number chosen be abc = 100a + 10b + c where, without losing any generality, it will be assumed that a > c.

Reversing the number gives $\qquad$ 100c + 10b + a

Subtracting then gives $\qquad$ 100a + 10b + c – (100c + 10b + a)

$$= 100(a - c) + (c - a)$$

However, c – a < 0 and so before this formula can be interpreted as a 3-digit number and reversed, it needs to be written in a slightly different form.

$$
\begin{aligned}
100(a - c) + (c - a) \quad &= 100(a - c - 1) + 100 + (c - a) \\
&= 100(a - c - 1) + 90 + (10 + c - a) \\
&= 100(a - c - 1) + 10 \times 9 + (10 + c - a)
\end{aligned}
$$

Now $0 \le a, c \le 9$ and c < a so that 0 < 10 + c – a < 10.

$\therefore$ 100(a – c) + (c – a) can be interpreted as a 3-digit number with digits a – c – 1, 9 and 10 + c – a. Reversing this and adding the reverse gives

$$
\begin{aligned}
100(a - c - 1) + 90 + (10 + c - a) &+ 100(10 + c - a) + 90 + a - c - 1 \\
&= 100(a - c - 1 + 10 + c - a) + 180 + 9 \\
&= 100 \times 9 + 180 + 9 \\
&= 1089
\end{aligned}
$$

4-digit variants

Let the 4-digit number chosen be 1000a + 100b + 10 c + d with a > d.

Reversing gives $\qquad$ 1000d + 100c + 10b + a

Subtracting then gives $\qquad$ 1000a + 100b + 10c + d – (1000d + 100c + 10b + a)

$$= 1000(a - d) + 100(b - c) + 10(c - b) + (d - a)$$

Case a) $\qquad$ b = c

The result of the subtraction is

$$1000(a - d) + d - a = 1000(a - d - 1) + 900 + 90 + 10 + d - a$$

which can be now be interpreted as a 4-digit number in a similar way to that described above.

Reversing this number and adding the reverse then gives

$$
\begin{aligned}
1000(a - d - 1) + 900 + 90 + 10 + d - a &+ 1000(10 + d - a) + 900 + 90 + (a - d - 1) \\
&= 1000(a - d - 1 + 10 + d - a) + 1800 + 180 + 9 \\
&= 1000 \times 9 + 1800 + 180 + 9 \\
&= 10989
\end{aligned}
$$

Case b) $b > c$

The result of the subtraction is
$$1000(a - d) + 100(b - c) + 10(c - b) + d - a$$
$$= 1000(a - d) + 100(b - c - 1) + 10(10 + c - b) + d - a$$
$$= 1000(a - d) + 100(b - c - 1) + 10(9 + c - b) + 10 + d - a$$
which can be now be interpreted as a 4-digit number in a similar way to that described above.
Reversing this number and adding the reverse then gives
$$1000(a - d) + 100(b - c - 1) + 10(9 + c - b) + 10 + d - a$$
$$+ 1000(10 + d - a) + 100(9 + c - b) + 10(b - c - 1) + a - d$$
$$= 1000(a - d + 10 + d - a) + 100(b - c - 1 + 9 + c - b) + 10(9 + c - b + b - c - 1) + 10$$
$$= 1000 \times 10 + 100 \times 8 + 10 \times 8 + 10$$
$$= 10000 + 800 + 80 + 10$$
$$= 10890$$

Case c) $b < c$

The result of the subtraction is
$$1000(a - d) + 100(b - c) + 10(c - b) + d - a$$
$$= 1000(a - d - 1) + 100(10 + b - c) + 10(c - b - 1) + 10 + d - a$$
which can be now be interpreted as a 4-digit number in a similar way to that described above.
Reversing this number and adding the reverse then gives
$$1000(a - d - 1) + 100(10 + b - c) + 10(c - b - 1) + 10 + d - a$$
$$+ 1000(10 + d - a) + 100(c - b - 1) + 10(10 + b - c) + a - d - 1$$
$$= 1000(a - d - 1 + 10 + d - a) + 100(10 + b - c + c - b - 1)$$
$$+ 10(c - b - 1 + 10 + b - c) + 9$$
$$= 1000 \times 9 + 100 \times 9 + 10 \times 9 + 9$$
$$= 9000 + 900 + 90 + 9$$
$$= 9999$$

The proofs for situations starting with 5-digit numbers follow in very similar fashion.

Number Trick A6

Ever Decreasing Numbers

Let the first digit of the 4-digit number be a. This means that the following digits will be a – 1, a – 2 and a – 3 respectively and the full number itself will be equal to
$$1000a + 100(a – 1) + 10(a – 2) + a – 3$$

Reversing now gives $\quad\quad 1000(a – 3) + 100(a – 2) + 10(a – 1) + a$
And subtracting then gives

$1000a + 100(a – 1) + 10(a – 2) + a – 3 – (1000(a – 3) + 100(a – 2) + 10(a – 1) + a)$
$= 1000(a – (a – 3)) + 100(a – 1 – (a – 2)) + 10(a – 2 – (a – 1)) + a – 3 – a$
$= 1000 \times 3 + 100 \times 1 + 10 \times (–1) + (–3)$
$= 3000 + 100 – 10 – 3$
$= 3087$

The proof of the 3-digit variant of this is very similar.

Let the first digit of the 3-digit number be a. This means that the following digits will be a – 1 and a – 2 respectively, and the full number itself will be equal to
$$100a + 10(a – 1) + a – 2$$

Reversing now gives $\quad\quad 100(a – 2) + 10(a – 1) + a$
And subtracting then gives

$\quad\quad 100a + 10(a – 1) + a – 2 – (100(a – 2) + 10(a – 1) + a)$
$\quad\quad = 100(a – (a – 2)) + 10(a – 1 – (a – 1)) + a – 2 – a$
$\quad\quad = 100 \times 2 + (–2)$
$\quad\quad = 200 – 2$
$\quad\quad = 198$

The variations where the digits decrease by 2 each time follow in a very similar way.

Let the first digit of the 4-digit number be a. This means that the following digits will be a – 2, a – 4 and a – 6 respectively, and the full number itself will be equal to
$$1000a + 100(a – 2) + 10(a – 4) + a – 6$$

Reversing now gives $\quad\quad 1000(a – 6) + 100(a – 4) + 10(a – 2) + a$
And subtracting then gives

$1000a + 100(a – 2) + 10(a – 4) + a – 6 – (1000(a – 6) + 100(a – 4) + 10(a – 2) + a)$
$\quad = 1000(a – (a – 6)) + 100(a – 2 – (a – 4)) + 10(a – 4 – (a – 2)) + a – 6 – a$
$\quad = 1000 \times 6 + 100 \times 2 + 10 \times (–2) + (–6)$
$\quad = 6000 + 200 – 20 – 6$
$\quad = 6174$

The proof of the 3-digit variant of this is very similar.

Let the first digit of the 3-digit number be a. This means that the following digits will be a – 2 and a – 4 respectively and the full number itself will be equal to
$$100a + 10(a - 2) + a - 4$$

Reversing now gives $\qquad 100(a - 4) + 10(a - 2) + a$
And subtracting then gives

$$100a + 10(a - 2) + a - 4 - (100(a - 4) + 10(a - 2) + a)$$
$$= 100(a - (a - 4)) + 10(a - 2 - (a - 2)) + a - 4 - a$$
$$= 100 \times 4 + (-4)$$
$$= 400 - 4$$
$$= 396$$

Number Trick A7

Dice, The Universe And Everything.

The reasons behind the working of this trick are quite simple. The process of selecting a value in the addition square and crossing out all other values in the same row and column isolates one number from the original numbers along the top of the square and one number from along the side which add to form the selected value in the square. Repeating this process until all the numbers in the square are either selected or crossed-out will isolate, in turn, all of the numbers from along the top and the side of the square and so the total obtained when the selected numbers are added will just be the total of the original numbers along the top and the side of the square. In the case of the square presented in the trick, this is just $2 \times (1 + 2 + 3 + 4 + 5 + 6) = 42$.

Number Trick A8

Multiplying Dice

The key to this trick is that the numbers on the opposite faces of a normal cubic die always add up to 7.

Let the two numbers rolled be a and b

1st multiplication	a × b	= ab
2nd multiplication	a × (7 – b)	= 7a – ab
3rd multiplication	(7 – a) × b	= 7b – ab
4th multiplication	(7 – a) × (7 – b)	= 49 – 7a – 7b + ab

$\therefore$ Sum = ab + 7a – ab + 7b – ab + 49 – 7a – 7b + ab = 49

In general, if the opposite faces of one die always add up to X and the opposite faces on the second die always add up to Y, the total obtained by multiplying the values in the four ways described and then adding will result in a final answer of X × Y.

Let the two numbers rolled be a and b

1st multiplication	a × b	= ab
2nd multiplication	a × (Y – b)	= Ya – ab
3rd multiplication	(X – a) × b	= Xb – ab
4th multiplication	(X – a) × (Y – b)	= XY – Ya – Xb + ab

$\therefore$ Sum = ab + Ya – ab + Xb – ab + XY – Ya – Xb + ab = XY

Number Trick A9

A Prime Example

To prove why this trick works, it is first necessary to show that any prime number above 3 is always one more or one less than a multiple of 6.

For any integer n, consider the six consecutive numbers 6n, 6n + 1, 6n + 2, 6n + 3, 6n + 4 and 6n + 5.

$$6n = 6 \times n \qquad \text{and so can never be prime}$$
$$6n + 2 = 2 \times (3n + 1) \qquad \text{and so can never be prime}$$
$$6n + 3 = 3 \times (2n + 1) \qquad \text{and so can never be prime}$$
$$6n + 4 = 2 \times (3n + 2) \qquad \text{and so can never be prime.}$$

Thus the only <u>possibilities</u> for prime numbers between two consecutive multiples of 6 are 6n + 1 and 6n + 5 (= 6(n + 1) – 1). This is not to say that all numbers of that form are prime – 49 and 65 are simple examples that disprove that hypothesis – but only that if a number is prime, then it must be of the form $6m \pm 1$ where m is an integer.

Let us now turn to proving why the trick itself works.

Let the prime chosen, p, be equal to $6m \pm 1$ for some integer m.

$$p^2 = (6m \pm 1)^2 = 36m^2 \pm 12m + 1$$
$$p^2 + 17 = 36m^2 \pm 12m + 18$$
$$(p^2 + 17) \div 12 = (36m^2 \pm 12m + 18) \div 12$$
$$= 3m^2 \pm m + 1 \text{ rem } 6$$

The variant suggested, where the division is by 4 rather than by 12, can be proved in an identical way.

$$(p^2 + 17) \div 4 = (36m^2 \pm 12m + 18) \div 4$$
$$= 9m^2 \pm 3m + 4 \text{ rem } 2$$

Number Trick A10

Elephant!

In proving why this particular trick works, I will first consider some more general results.

Result 1:
Any number is divisible by 9 if and only if the sum of its digits is divisible by 9.

Let the number $N = x_n \times 10^n + x_{n-1} \times 10^{n-1} + \ldots + x_2 \times 10^2 + x_1 \times 10^1 + x_0$. This represents an n+1-digit number with digits $x_n, x_{n-1}, \ldots, x_2, x_1$ and x_0.

Now, for $n \geq 1$, $\quad 10^n - 1 = (10 - 1)(10^{n-1} + 10^{n-2} + \ldots + 10^2 + 10^1 + 1)$
$$= 9 \times (10^{n-1} + 10^{n-2} + \ldots + 10^2 + 10^1 + 1) \qquad (*)$$

Hence the expression for N can be rewritten as

$$N = x_n \times (10^n - 1) + x_{n-1} \times (10^{n-1} - 1) + \ldots + x_2 \times (10^2 - 1) + x_1 \times (10^1 - 1)$$
$$+ x_n + x_{n-1} + \ldots + x_2 + x_1 + x_0.$$

From (*) each of the expressions of the form $10^m - 1$ is a multiple of 9 and so

$$N = 9 \times A + x_n + x_{n-1} + \ldots + x_2 + x_1 + x_0 \text{ for some integer A.}$$

As $9 \times A$ will always be divisible by 9, any number N will be divisible by 9 precisely when the sum of its digits $x_n + x_{n-1} + \ldots + x_2 + x_1 + x_0$ is divisible by 9.

This result also implies a second result.

Result 2:
The remainder when a number is divided by 9 will be exactly the same as the remainder obtained when the sum of its digits is divisible by 9.

If $N = 9X + r$ where $0 \leq r \leq 8$ then, using the formulation above,
$$9 \times A + x_n + x_{n-1} + \ldots + x_2 + x_1 + x_0 = 9X + r$$
$$\therefore x_n + x_{n-1} + \ldots + x_2 + x_1 + x_0 = 9 \times (X - A) + r$$

Thus the remainder, r, obtained when N is divided by 9, is the same as the remainder obtained when the sum of its digits is divided by 9.

Having established these more general results, I can now go on to prove why this particular trick works.

Using result 1 repeatedly, if the digits of a large multiple of 9 are added and the process repeated until a single digit occurs, this single digit has to be 9. Once this single figure has been forced, all the manipulations that follow are specified.

$$X \to X + 2 \to 3(X + 2) = 3X + 6 \to 3X + 12 \to 3(3X + 12) = 9X + 36 = 9(X + 3)$$

144

Thus the number obtained by the initial manipulations is a multiple of 9 and so will reduce to 9 when its digits are added repeatedly.

$$9(X + 3) \rightarrow 9 \rightarrow 4$$

The only country in Europe whose name begins with D is Denmark and so that will be the country chosen (particularly if you help your audience with the list of countries as suggested) and that means that the mammal to be chosen must begin with E. Although there are other possible choices for the mammal, such as an eland, no other mammal beginning with E is as well known as an elephant and so this will invariably be the mammal chosen.

Number Trick A11

It's Magic!

As was the case with the previous trick, the key here is to produce a multiple of 9 and then add digits, forcing a 9 to be the value used at a particular stage of the trick. Once this value has been produced, the rest of the trick is self-working. The multiplication by 9 within this trick is much more overt than in the previous trick although it does use other seemingly random steps to try and hide that key fact.

Part B

Back Where You Started

Number Trick B1

Back To The Beginning (1)

In most cases, as in Number Tricks Part A, the number chosen will be taken to be X to avoid any confusion with the multiplication sign.

Version 1

$X \rightarrow 2X \rightarrow 2X + 16 \rightarrow X + 8 \rightarrow X$

Version 2

$X \rightarrow 2X \rightarrow 2X + 10 \rightarrow 2(2X + 10) = 4X + 20 \rightarrow 4X + 28 \rightarrow X + 7 \rightarrow X$

Version 3

$X \rightarrow 3X \rightarrow 3X + 2 \rightarrow 4(3X + 2) = 12X + 8 \rightarrow 12X + 20 \rightarrow 6X + 10 \rightarrow 6X + 6 \rightarrow X + 1 \rightarrow X$

Number Trick B2

Back To The Beginning (2)

Version 1

$$X \rightarrow X^2 \rightarrow X^2 - 4 \rightarrow (X^2 - 4) \div (X - 2) = (X + 2) \times (X - 2) \div (X - 2) = X + 2 \rightarrow X$$

Version 2

$$X \rightarrow X \times (X + 4) = X^2 + 4X \rightarrow X^2 + 4X + 4 = (X + 2)^2 \rightarrow \sqrt{(X + 2)^2} = X + 2 \rightarrow X$$

Version 3

$$X \rightarrow 4X \rightarrow 4X \times (X + 1) = 4X^2 + 4X \rightarrow 4X^2 + 4X + 1 = (2X + 1)^2$$
$$\rightarrow \sqrt{(2X + 1)^2} = 2X + 1 \rightarrow 2X \rightarrow X$$

Version 4

$$X \rightarrow X^2 \rightarrow X^2 + 6X \rightarrow X^2 + 6X + 9 = (X + 3)^2 \rightarrow \sqrt{(X + 3)^2} = X + 3 \rightarrow X$$

Version 5

$$X \rightarrow X^3 \rightarrow X^3 - 8 \rightarrow (X^3 - 8) \div (X - 2) = (X^2 + 2X + 4) \times (X - 2) \div (X - 2)$$
$$= X^2 + 2X + 4 \rightarrow X^2 + 3X + 4 \rightarrow X^2 + 4X + 4 = (X + 2)^2 \rightarrow \sqrt{(X + 2)^2}$$
$$= X + 2 \rightarrow X$$

Number Trick B3

Digit Addition

Version 1

$$X \rightarrow X + 9 = 10 + (X - 1) \rightarrow 1 + X - 1 = X$$

$1 \leq X \leq 10 \Rightarrow 0 \leq X - 1 \leq 9$

$\therefore 10 + X - 1$ is the 2-digit number with digits 1 and $X - 1$, allowing the addition of digits to occur as shown.

Version 2

$$X \rightarrow X + 9 \rightarrow 2(X + 9) = 2X + 18 \rightarrow X + 18 = 20 + (X - 2) \rightarrow 2 + X - 2 = X$$

$2 \leq X \leq 11 \Rightarrow 0 \leq X - 2 \leq 9$

$\therefore 20 + X - 2$ is the 2-digit number with digits 2 and $X - 2$, allowing the addition of digits to occur as shown.

Version 3

$$X \rightarrow X + 6 \rightarrow 3(X + 6) = 3X + 18 \rightarrow 2X + 18 \rightarrow X + 9 = 10 + (X - 1)$$
$$\rightarrow 1 + X - 1 = X$$

$1 \leq X \leq 10 \Rightarrow 0 \leq X - 1 \leq 9$

$\therefore 10 + X - 1$ is the 2-digit number with digits 1 and $X - 1$, allowing the addition of digits to occur as shown.

Version 4

$$X \rightarrow X + 3 \rightarrow 2(X + 3) = 2X + 6 \rightarrow 2X + 9 \rightarrow X + 9 = 10 + (X - 1) \rightarrow 1 + X - 1 = X$$

$1 \leq X \leq 10 \Rightarrow 0 \leq X - 1 \leq 9$

$\therefore 10 + X - 1$ is the 2-digit number with digits 1 and $X - 1$ allowing, the addition of digits to occur as shown.

Version 5

$$X \rightarrow X + 20 \rightarrow 3(X + 20) = 3X + 60 \rightarrow 2X + 60 \rightarrow X + 30 \rightarrow X + 27 = 30 + (X - 3)$$
$$\rightarrow 3 + X - 3 = X$$

$3 \leq X \leq 12 \Rightarrow 0 \leq X - 3 \leq 9$

$\therefore 30 + X - 3$ is the 2-digit number with digits 3 and $X - 3$, allowing the addition of digits to occur as shown.

Version 6

If the number chosen is between 10 and 19, it can be written as $10 + X$ with $0 \leq X \leq 9$.

$10 + X \rightarrow 80 + X \rightarrow 10(80 + X) = 800 + 10X \rightarrow 800 + 10X + 2 \rightarrow 8 + X + 2$
$= 10 + X$

Version 7

If the number chosen is between 20 and 29, it can be written as $20 + X$ with $0 \leq X \leq 9$.

$20 + X \rightarrow 80 + X \rightarrow 8 + X \rightarrow 8 + X + 12 = 20 + X$

Number Trick B4

Digit Subtraction

Version 1

$$X \rightarrow 2X \rightarrow 2X + 7 \rightarrow 5(2X + 7) = 10X + 35 \rightarrow 10X + 33 = 10(X + 3) + 3$$
$$\rightarrow X + 3 - 3 = X$$

Version 2

$$X \rightarrow 2X \rightarrow 2X + 3 \rightarrow 5(2X + 3) = 10X + 15 \rightarrow 10X + 11 = 10(X + 1) + 1$$
$$\rightarrow X + 1 - 1 = X$$

Version 3

$$X \rightarrow 3X \rightarrow 3X + 6 \rightarrow 3(3X + 6) = 9X + 18 \rightarrow 9X + 26 \rightarrow 10X + 26$$
$$\rightarrow 10X + 22 = 10(X + 2) + 2 \rightarrow X + 2 - 2 = X$$

Number Trick B5

Multiply Up And Divide Down

Version 1

$X \rightarrow 3X \rightarrow 5 \times 3X = 15X \rightarrow 16X \rightarrow 16X \div 2 = 8X \rightarrow X$

Version 2

$X \rightarrow 9X \rightarrow 7 \times 9X = 63X \rightarrow 64X \rightarrow 64X \div 2 = 32X \rightarrow 32X \div 4 = 8X \rightarrow X$

Version 3

$X \rightarrow 7X \rightarrow 5 \times 7X = 35X \rightarrow 3 \times 35X = 105X \rightarrow 104X \rightarrow 104X \div 2 = 52X \rightarrow 52X \div 4 = 13X \rightarrow X$

Number Trick B6

Repeating Sequences (1)

Version 1

$$X \rightarrow 37X \rightarrow 3 \times 37X = 111X$$

Version 2

$$X \rightarrow 271X \rightarrow 41 \times 271X = 11111X$$

Version 3

$$X \rightarrow 37X \rightarrow 13 \times 37X = 481X \rightarrow 11 \times 481X = 5291X \rightarrow 7 \times 5291X = 37037X$$
$$\rightarrow 3 \times 37037X = 111111X$$

Version 4

$$X \rightarrow 12345679X \rightarrow 9 \times 12345679X = 111111111X$$

Version 5

Consider the 2-digit number with digits X and Y as $10X + Y$.

$$10X + Y \rightarrow 37 \times (10X + Y) = 370X + 37Y \rightarrow 13 \times (370X + 10Y) = 4810X + 481Y$$
$$\rightarrow 7 \times (4810X + 481Y) = 36670X + 3667Y \rightarrow 3 \times (33670X + 3367Y) =$$
$$101010X + 10101Y = 100000X + 10000Y + 1000X + 100Y + 10X + Y$$

Version 6

Consider the 3-digit number with digits X, Y and Z as $100X + 10Y + Z$.

$$100X + 10Y + Z \rightarrow 13 \times (100X + 10Y + Z) = 1300X + 130Y + 13Z$$
$$\rightarrow 11 \times (1300X + 130Y + 13Z) = 14300X + 1430Y + 143Z$$
$$\rightarrow 3 \times (14300X + 1430Y + 143Z) = 100100X + 10010Y + 1001Z$$
$$= 100000X + 10000Y + 1000Z + 100X + 10Y + Z$$

Version 7

$$X \rightarrow XXXXXX = 111111X \rightarrow 111111X \div 3 = 37037X \rightarrow 37037X \div 7 = 5291X \rightarrow$$
$$5291X \div 11 = 481X \rightarrow 481X \div 13 = 37X \rightarrow X$$

Number Trick B7

Repeating Sequences (2)

Version 1

$X \rightarrow 16X \rightarrow 7 \times 16X = 112X \rightarrow 111X$

Version 2

$X \rightarrow 139X \rightarrow 8 \times 139X = 1112X \rightarrow 1111X$

Version 3

$X \rightarrow 463X \rightarrow 8 \times 463X = 3704X \rightarrow 3 \times 3704X = 11112X \rightarrow 11111X$

Version 4

$X \rightarrow 43X \rightarrow 19 \times 43X = 817X \rightarrow 17 \times 817X = 13889X \rightarrow 8 \times 13889X = 111112X \rightarrow 111111X$

Version 5

Consider the 2-digit number with digits X and Y as $10X + Y$.

$10X + Y \rightarrow 17 \times (10X + Y) = 170X + 17Y \rightarrow 6 \times (170X + 17Y) = 1020X + 102Y \rightarrow 1020X + 102Y - 10X - Y = 1010X + 101Y = 1000X + 100Y + 10X + Y$

Number Trick B8

A Magic Number

Consider the 4-digit number with digits X, Y, Z and W as $1000X + 100Y + 10Z + W$.

1st digit	X
1st two digits	$XY = 10X + Y$
1st three digits	$XYZ = 100X + 10Y + Z$

Summing gives

$$X + 10X + Y + 100X + 10Y + Z = 111X + 11Y + Z$$

Multiplying by 9 gives

$$9 \times (111X + 11Y + Z) = 999X + 99Y + 9Z$$

Adding the digits gives

$$999X + 99Y + 9Z + X + Y + Z + W$$
$$= 1000X + 100Y + 10Z + W$$

Number Trick B9

Number Reversal

Note: a 2-digit number with digits Y and X is equal to $10Y + X$.

Version 1

$10(X + 3) + X \rightarrow 10(X + 3) + X - 27 = 10X + 30 + X - 27 = 10X + (X + 3)$
$\rightarrow 10(X + 3) + X$

General extension

$10(X + A) + X \rightarrow 10(X + A) + X - 9A = 10X + 10A + X - 9A = 10X + (X + A)$
$\rightarrow 10(X + A) + X$

Note: a 3-digit number with digits Z, Y and X is equal to $100Z + 10Y + X$.

Version 2

$100(X + 3) + 10Y + X \rightarrow 100(X + 3) + 10Y + X - 297$
$= 100X + 300 + 10Y + X - 297 = 100X + 10Y + (X + 3) \rightarrow 100(X + 3) + 10Y + X$

General extension

$100(X + A) + 10Y + X \rightarrow 100(X + A) + 10Y + X - 99A$
$= 100X + 100A + 10Y + X - 99A = 100X + 10Y + (X + A)$
$\rightarrow 100(X + A) + 10Y + X$

Note: a 4-digit number with digits W, Z, Y and X is equal to
$1000W + 100Z + 10Y + X$.

Version 3

$1000(X + 3) + 100(Y + 2) + 10Y + X \rightarrow 1000(X + 3) + 100(Y + 2) + 10Y + X - 2997$
$= 1000X + 3000 + 100Y + 200 + 10Y + X - 2997$
$= 1000X + 100Y + 200 + 10Y + (X + 3)$
$\rightarrow 1000X + 100Y + 200 + 10Y + (X + 3) - 180$
$= 1000X + 100Y + 10Y + 20 + (X + 3) = 1000X + 100Y + 10(Y + 2) + (X + 3)$
$\rightarrow 1000(X + 3) + 100(Y + 2) + 10Y + X$

General extension

$1000(X + A) + 100(Y + B) + 10Y + X$
$\rightarrow 1000(X + A) + 100(Y + B) + 10Y + X - 999A$
$= 1000X + 1000A + 100Y + 100B + 10Y + X - 999A$
$= 1000X + 100Y + 100B + 10Y + (X + A)$
$\rightarrow 1000X + 100Y + 100B + 10Y + (X + A) - 90B$
$= 1000X + 100Y + 10Y + 10B + (X + A) = 1000X + 100Y + 10(Y + B) + (X + A)$
$\rightarrow 1000(X + A) + 100(Y + B) + 10Y + X$

Part C

Mind Reading Tricks

Number Trick C1

One Number Tricks

Version 1

Let the number chosen be X (as in the earlier sections to avoid confusion with the multiplication sign).

$X \rightarrow 2X \rightarrow 2X + 3 \rightarrow 5(2X + 3) = 10X + 15 \rightarrow 10X + 11 = 10X + 10 + 1$
$= 10(X + 1) + 1$

The units digit of their answer will always be 1. Subtracting this from the remainder of the number, which will be X + 1, will always give X.

Version 2

Let the number chosen be 2X + 1. This is to ensure that the number being considered is odd as required.

$2X + 1 \rightarrow 3(2X + 1) = 6X + 3 \rightarrow 6X + 4 \rightarrow 3(6X + 4) = 18X + 12 \rightarrow (18X + 12)/2$
$= 9X + 6 \rightarrow X$ remainder 6 and so their final answer will be given as X.

To get their original number, simply double the answer and add 1: $X \rightarrow 2X + 1$

Version 3

Let the tens digit of the number chosen be X.
∴ The units digit of the number will be 11 – X
and the full number will be 10X + 11 – X

$10X + 11 - X \rightarrow 10X + 11 - X + 2X = 11X + 11 = 11(X + 1) \rightarrow X + 1$

Subtracting 1 from their answer will always give you the value of X, the tens digit of their number. Subtracting this number from 11 will then give you the units digit.

Version 4

Let the number chosen be X.

$X \rightarrow 10X \rightarrow 10X + X = 11X \rightarrow 33X \rightarrow 11 \times 33X = 363X \rightarrow 3 \times 363X = 1089X$
$= 1000X + 100X - 10X - X$
$= 1000X + 100X - 100 + 90 - 10X + 10 - X$
$= 1000X + 100(X - 1) + 10(9 - X) + 10 - X$

As $1 \le X \le 9$, the values of all of the expressions X, $X - 1$, $9 - X$ and $10 - X$ lie in the range 0 to 9. This means that $1000X + 100(X - 1) + 10(9 - X) + 10 - X$ represents a 4-digit number with digits X, $X - 1$, $9 - X$ and $10 - X$.

Subtracting their value, the final digit of their answer, from 10 will then give you X, (because $10 - (10 - X) = X$) the number chosen and the other digits of their answer can then be calculated from that.

Version 5
Let the number chosen be X.

$$X \rightarrow 43X \rightarrow 7 \times 43X = 301X = 300X + X$$

Now $X < 100$ and so the final two digits of their answer represent the number X. The remainder of the number will represent $3X$ and so dividing the value given by 3 will give you the value of X.

Number Trick C2

Two Number Tricks

Version 1
Let the two numbers chosen be X and Y.

$$X \rightarrow 2X \rightarrow 2X + 3 \rightarrow 5(2X + 3) = 10X + 15 \rightarrow 10X + 15 + Y$$

Subtracting 15 leaves 10X + Y which, because both X and Y are less than 10, represents the 2-digit number with digits X and Y.

Version 2
Let the two numbers chosen be X and Y.

$$X \rightarrow X - 2 \rightarrow 5(X - 2) = 5X - 10 \rightarrow 5X - 10 + Y \rightarrow 2(5X - 10 + Y)$$
$$= 10X - 20 + 2Y \rightarrow 10X - 11 + 2Y \rightarrow 10X - 11 + Y = 10X - 10 - 1 + Y$$
$$= 10(X - 1) + (Y - 1)$$

As both X and Y are less than 10, X – 1 and Y – 1 are less than 9 and so the number 10(X – 1) + (Y – 1) represents the 2-digit number with digits X – 1 and Y – 1.

Version 3
Let the smaller number chosen be X and the larger number chosen be Y.

$$X + Y \rightarrow 10(X + Y) = 10X + 10Y \rightarrow 10X + 11Y \rightarrow 9X + 11Y = 10X - X + 10Y + Y$$
$$= 10(Y + X) + (Y - X)$$

As both X and Y are under 10, Y – X will also be under 10 and so the units digit of the expression 10(Y + X) + (Y – X) will be Y – X, while the remainder of the number represents Y + X.

The secret step implies the calculations
$$Y + X - (Y - X) = 2X \qquad 2X \div 2 = X \qquad \text{to obtain the smaller number}$$
and
$$Y + X + (Y - X) = 2Y \qquad 2Y \div 2 = Y \qquad \text{to obtain the larger number.}$$

Version 4
Let the smaller number chosen be X and the larger number chosen be Y.

$$X + Y \rightarrow 5(X + Y) = 5X + 5Y \rightarrow 6X + 5Y \rightarrow 2(6X + 5Y) = 12X + 10Y$$
$$\rightarrow 11X + 10Y \rightarrow 11X + 10Y - 1 = 10X + X + 10Y - 1 = 10(X + Y) + (X - 1)$$

As X is less than 10, X – 1 is less than 9 so the units digit of the answer will be X – 1 and adding 1 to this will give the value of X. The remainder of the answer will be the number X + Y, so subtracting the now known value of X from this will give the value of Y.

Version 5

Let the smaller number chosen be X and the larger number chosen be Y.

$Y - X \rightarrow 10(Y - X) = 10Y - 10X \rightarrow 10Y - 9X \rightarrow 10Y - 9X - 1$
$\quad\quad = 10Y - 10X + X - 1 = 10(Y - X) + (X - 1)$

As X is less than 10, X − 1 is less than 9 so the units digit of the answer will be X − 1 and adding 1 to this will give the value of X. The remainder of the answer will be the number Y − X, so adding the now known value of X to this will give the value of Y.

Number Trick C3

Birthday Tricks

Version 1

Let the number of the month be m and the number of the day be d.

$$m \rightarrow 5m \rightarrow 5m + 6 \rightarrow 4(5m + 6) = 20m + 24 \rightarrow 20m + 33 \rightarrow 5(20m + 33)$$
$$= 100m + 165 \rightarrow 100m + 165 + d$$

Subtracting 165 from this leaves $100m + d$ and, as $1 \leq d \leq 31$, the final two digits of this will represent the value of d while the remainder of the number will represent the value of m.

Version 2

Let the number of the month be m and the number of the day be d.

$$m \rightarrow 2m \rightarrow 2m + 5 \rightarrow 50(2m + 5) = 100m + 250 \rightarrow 100m + 250 + d$$
$$\rightarrow 100m - 115 + d$$

Adding 115 to this leaves $100m + d$ and, as $1 \leq d \leq 31$, the final two digits of this will represent the value of d while the remainder of the number will represent the value of m.

Number Trick C4

Age Finder

Version 1
Let the number chosen be X and let their age be Y.

$$X \rightarrow 9X \rightarrow 10Y - 9X \rightarrow 10Y - 9X - 1 = 10Y - 10X + X - 1 = 10(Y - X) + X - 1$$

As X is less than 10, $X - 1$ is less than 9 and so the units digit of their answer is $X - 1$. Adding 1 to this allows the value of X to be found and then, using this now known value, the value of Y can be found by adding X to the remainder of their answer which is representing $Y - X$.

Version 2a
Let your age be X and their age be Y with $X < Y$.

$$99 - X \rightarrow 99 - X + Y \rightarrow 99 - X + Y - 100 + 1 = Y - X$$

The secret step tells you to add your age, implying the calculation
$$Y - X + X = Y.$$

Version 2b
Let your age be X and their age be Y with $X > Y$.

$$99 + X \rightarrow 99 + X - Y \rightarrow 99 + X - Y - 100 + 1 = X - Y$$

The secret step tells you to subtract this from your age, implying the calculation
$$X - (X - Y) = Y.$$

Number Trick C5

Scramble

In Number Trick A10, it was proved that in any multiple of 9, the sum of the digits must also be a multiple of 9 and, similarly, that any number and the sum of the digits of that number leave the same remainder when divided by 9.

To prove why this specific trick works, consider the following argument:

Rearranging the digits of a number does not alter the sum of these digits and hence, using the second of the general results proved in A10, both the original number and the number formed by rearranging its digits will have the same remainder when divided by 9.

$$\therefore \text{ if } N = 9X + r \text{ then } N^* = 9Y + r$$

where N^* represents the number formed by rearranging the digits of N. Subtracting the larger of these from the smaller will, therefore, result in a number that is divisible by 9, which implies that the sum of the digits of that difference will be divisible by 9. Should this sum of digits be itself a number with more than one digit, applying the result repeatedly will result in the single digit 9 being reached as the sum of the digits of any multiple of 9. However, if a non-zero digit is removed from this difference and its digits then summed, the final value would not then be 9. The value of the removed digit can then be determined by subtracting the final value from 9, unless the digit removed was itself 9 in which case the final value of 9 would still be obtained.

Number Trick C6

Consecutive Numbers

Version 1
Let the numbers chosen be $n - 1$, n and $n + 1$.
Total $= n - 1 + n + n + 1 = 3n$.

Let the multiple of 3 called out be $3x$.
New total $= 3n + 3x = 3(n + x)$.

Multiplying by 67 gives $3(n + x) \times 67 = 201(n + x) = 200(n + x) + (n + x)$

Now
$$3x < 100 \Rightarrow x < 34 \text{ and } n < 60 \text{ so } n + x < 94.$$

This means that the final two figures of $201(n + x)$ will be $n + x$.

Subtracting x, i.e. subtracting ⅓ of the number called out, from the last two digits of their answer will give n, the middle number of the three numbers chosen.

Version 2
Let the numbers chosen be $n - 1$, n and $n + 1$.
Total $= n - 1 + n + n + 1 = 3n$.

Let the multiple of 3 called out be $3x$.
New total $= 3n + 3x = 3(n + x)$.

Multiplying by 34 gives $3(n + x) \times 34 = 102(n + x) = 100(n + x) + 2(n + x)$

Now
$$3x < 50 \Rightarrow x < 17 \text{ and } n < 33 \text{ so } n + x < 50 \text{ and hence } 2(n + x) < 100.$$

This means that the final two figures of $102(n + x)$ will be $2(n + x)$.

Dividing the last two digits of their answer by 2 will then give $n + x$ and subtracting x, i.e. subtracting ⅓ of the number called out, from this will give n, the middle number of the three numbers chosen.

Version 3

Let the numbers chosen be n – 3, n – 2, n – 1, n, n + 1 and n + 2.

Total = n – 3 + n – 2 + n – 1 + n + n + 1 + n + 2 = 6n – 3.

Let the multiple of 6 called out be 6x.

New total = 6n – 3 + 6x.

Adding 3 makes the total = 6n – 3 + 6 x + 3 = 6n + 6x = 6(n + x).

Multiplying by 17 gives 6(n + x) × 17 = 102(n + x) = 100(n + x) + 2(n + x)

Now

$$6x < 100 \Rightarrow x < 17 \text{ and } n + 2 < 35 \Rightarrow n < 33$$

so n + x < 50 and hence 2(n + x) < 100.

This means that the final two figures of 102(n + x) will be 2(n + x).

Dividing the last two digits of their answer by 2 will then give n + x and subtracting x, i.e. subtracting a sixth of the number called out, from this will give n, the fourth number of the six numbers chosen.

Version 4

Let the numbers chosen be n – 3, n – 2, n – 1, n, n + 1, n + 2 and n + 3.

Total = n – 3 + n – 2 + n – 1 + n + n + 1 + n + 2 + n + 3 = 7n.

Let the multiple of 7 called out be 7x.

New total = 7n + 7x = 7(n + x).

Multiplying by 43 gives 7(n + x) × 43 = 301(n + x) = 300(n + x) + (n + x)

Now

$$7x < 100 \Rightarrow x < 15 \text{ and } n < 80 \text{ so } n + x < 95.$$

This means that the final two figures of 301(n + x) will be (n + x).

Subtracting x, i.e. subtracting a seventh of the number called out, from the last two digits of their answer will give n, the middle number of the seven numbers chosen.

Number Trick C7

Split

This trick was one I found presented on the Internet as part of a collection of maths games, puzzles and resources at www.greenleecds.com/mathdownloads.html. The thing that makes this trick different is in its proof as it is the first magic trick I've seen that uses the process of mathematical induction to show why it actually works.

To prove: The final result from selecting A matches is $A(A-1)/2$.

Consider the case when $A = 1$.
This pile cannot be split which means no multiplication step is possible and so a final total of 0 is obtained.
Now $1(1-1)/2 = 0$ and so the result is true for $A = 1$.

Consider the case when $A = 2$.
Obviously the only way a pile of two matches can be split is into two piles of one match, giving a multiplication step of $1 \times 1 = 2$ which would also be the final total as no further splitting is possible.
Now $2(2-1)/2 = 1$ and so the result is true for $A = 2$.

This is now where the induction step comes in. We will assume that the result is true for all possible values of A up to and including $A = N - 1$ and then consider a pile of N matches. Assume this pile is split into two smaller piles of X and Y matches respectively where $1 \leq X, Y \leq N - 1$.

From the induction step, we know that the result hold for a pile of X matches which would give a total of $X(X-1)/2$ and for a pile of Y matches which would give a total of $Y(Y-1)/2$.

$\therefore$ The total for $X + Y$ matches would be

$$\text{total for X matches} + \text{total for Y matches} + X \times Y$$
$$= X(X-1)/2 + Y(Y-1)/2 + XY$$
$$= (X^2 - X + Y^2 - Y + 2XY)/2$$
$$= ((X+Y)^2 - (X+Y))/2$$
$$= (X+Y)(X+Y-1)/2$$
$$= N(N-1)/2$$

As this is in the same form as the desired expression, we can now say that if the result is true for all values of A up to and including $N - 1$, then it will also be true for all values of A up to and including N. As the result is true for $A = 1$ and $A = 2$, we can then conclude that the result will be true for all $A \geq 1$.

Number Trick C8

Three Digit Numbers

The proof of this is quite tricky as it involves modulo arithmetic.

Let the three digits chosen be X, Y and Z.

It is possible to make six different 3-digit numbers using these three digits but, according to the rubric of the trick, only five are required to be added. Let the 3-digit number not used be $XYZ = 100X + 10Y + Z$.

Adding all six possible 3-digit numbers would give a total of $222(X + Y + Z)$ so the value of the total of the five numbers added, N, is given by

$$N = 222(X + Y + Z) - 100X - 10Y - Z$$

Rearranging this expression gives

$$100X + 10Y + Z = 222(X + Y + Z) - N \qquad (*)$$

This means to find the unused 3-digit number, we appear to need to find the value of $X + Y + Z$. However, this will not be necessary. Working in arithmetic modulo 9, we will find the value of $X + Y + Z$ (mod 9), use this to find an initial estimate for the unused 3-digit number and then add multiples of $1998 = 222 \times 9$ to that estimate until the required value is obtained.

Note:
When working modulo 9, any number has the same value as the sum of its digits. This was proved as part of the explanation of Number Trick A10 and referred to in Number Trick C5. Also the digit sum of twice a number and twice the digit sum of a number will have the same value modulo 9, which I will now prove here.

Consider the number P with digits $x_n, x_{n-1}, \ldots, x_2, x_1$ and x_0 and let

$$P = 9Q + r \text{ with } 0 \leq r \leq 8.$$

Using the result proved in Number Trick A10,

$$x_n + x_{n-1} + \ldots + x_2 + x_1 + x_0 = 9A + r.$$

Using these expressions,

$$2P = 2(9Q + r) = 18Q + 2r = 9(2Q) + 2r \Rightarrow 2P \equiv 2r \text{ (mod 9)}$$

and

$$2(x_n + x_{n-1} + \ldots + x_2 + x_1 + x_0) = 2(9A + r) = 18A + 2r = 9(2A) + 2r$$
$$\Rightarrow 2(x_n + x_{n-1} + \ldots + x_2 + x_1 + x_0) \equiv 2r \text{ (mod 9)}.$$

Hence the digit sum of twice a number and twice the digit sum of the same number will have the same value modulo 9.

Now consider the value of 2N

$$2N = 444(X + Y + Z) - 200X - 20Y - 2Z$$
$$\therefore 2N = X + Y + Z + 243X + 423Y + 441Z$$
$$\therefore 2N = X + Y + Z + 9(27X + 47Y + 49Z)$$
$$\therefore 2N \equiv X + Y + Z \ (\text{mod } 9)$$

Therefore, applying the result proved above we know that twice the digit sum of N is equal to $X + Y + Z \ (\text{mod } 9)$. Thus, once we have this value for $X + Y + Z \ (\text{mod } 9)$, which is equivalent to finding the remainder when $X + Y + Z$ is divided by 9, we can substitute this into (*) and obtain an initial estimate for the unused number. If we then remember that

$$X + Y + Z \equiv R \ (\text{mod } 9) \text{ means } X + Y + Z = 9k + R \text{ for some integer k}$$

it can be seen from (*) that

$$100X + 10Y + Z = 222(9k + R) - N \Rightarrow 100X + 10Y + Z = 1998k + 222R - N$$

and so adding 1998 repeatedly to $222R - N$, until a positive value is obtained will give the required 3-digit number.

Number Trick C9

Remainders

The mathematics behind the creation of these tricks is an application of an aspect of Number Theory known as the Chinese Remainder Theorem. The full details of how this theory is applied to create the tricks and what it actually means are explained in Appendix 1 and so here I will simply demonstrate that the tricks described do work using the indicated formulae.

Version 1

Let the number chosen be n

$\therefore$ n = 3X + r where $0 \leq r \leq 2$ is the remainder obtained when n is divided by 3

Also n = 4Y + s where $0 \leq s \leq 3$ is the remainder obtained when n is divided by 4

and n = 5Z + t where $0 \leq t \leq 4$ is the remainder obtained when n is divided by 5

$$\begin{aligned}
\therefore \ 40r + 45s + 36t &= 40(n - 3X) + 45(n - 4Y) + 36(n - 5Z) \\
&= 40n - 120X + 45n - 180Y + 36n - 180Z \\
&= 121n - 120X - 180Y - 180Z \\
&= n + 120n - 120X - 180Y - 180Z \\
&= n + 60(2n - 2X - 3Y - 3Z)
\end{aligned}$$

This analysis implies that the given formula will give an answer of the form n + 60k. Subtracting multiples of 60 until the number obtained is in the range 1 to 60 will therefore isolate n.

Version 2

Let the number chosen be n

$\therefore$ n = 3X + r where $0 \leq r \leq 2$ is the remainder obtained when n is divided by 3

Also n = 5Y + s where $0 \leq s \leq 4$ is the remainder obtained when n is divided by 5

and n = 7Z + t where $0 \leq t \leq 6$ is the remainder obtained when n is divided by 7

$$\begin{aligned}
\therefore \ 70r + 21s + 315 &= 70(n - 3X) + 21(n - 5Y) + 15(n - 7Z) \\
&= 70n - 210X + 21n - 105Y + 15n - 105Z \\
&= 106n - 210X - 105Y - 105Z \\
&= n + 105n - 210X - 105Y - 105Z \\
&= n + 105(n - 2X - Y - Z)
\end{aligned}$$

This analysis implies that the given formula will give an answer of the form n + 105k. Subtracting multiples of 105 until the number obtained is in the range 1 to 100 will therefore isolate n.

Version 3

Let the number chosen be n

$\therefore$ n = 7X + r where $0 \leq r \leq 6$ is the remainder obtained when n is divided by 7

Also n = 11Y + s where $0 \leq s \leq 10$ is the remainder obtained when n is divided by 11

and n = 13Z + t where $0 \leq t \leq 12$ is the remainder obtained when n is divided by 13

$$\begin{aligned}
\therefore\ 715r + 364s + 924t &= 715(n - 7X) + 364(n - 11Y) + 924(n - 13Z) \\
&= 715n - 5005X + 364n - 4004Y + 924n - 12012Z \\
&= 2003n - 5005X - 4004Y - 12012Z \\
&= n + 2002n - 5005X - 4004Y - 12012Z \\
&= n + 1001(2n - 5X - 4Y - 12Z)
\end{aligned}$$

This analysis implies that the given formula will give an answer of the form n + 1001k. Subtracting multiples of 1001 until the number obtained is in the range 1 to 1000 will therefore isolate n.

Similar versions that can be used include

- Using the formula 36r + 28s and subtracting 63 repeatedly to find a number between 1 and 63 where r and s are remainders from dividing the number by 7 and 9 respectively.
- Using the formula 210r + 190s and subtracting 399 repeatedly to find a number between 1 and 399 where r and s are remainders from dividing the number by 19 and 21 respectively.
- Using the formula 51r + 34s + 18t and subtracting 102 repeatedly to find a number between 1 and 102 where r, s and t are remainders from dividing the number by 2, 3 and 17 respectively.
- Using the formula 416r + 560s + 65t and subtracting 1040 repeatedly to find a number between 1 and 1040 where r, s and t are remainders from dividing the number by 5, 13 and 16 respectively.
- Using the formula 280r + 105s + 336t + 120u and subtracting 420 repeatedly to find a number between 1 and 420 where r, s, t and u are remainders from dividing the number by 3, 4, 5 and 7 respectively.

Number Trick C10

Choices (1)

The mathematics presented to show why this trick works will be quite limited. I will simply show numerically that the six possible arrangements of choice of cards will leave the different numbers of matches stated.

Recall that the first, second and third volunteers are initially given one, two and three matches respectively, then asked to choose one of three cards labelled A, B and C before taking more matches from the remaining pile of 18 according to the instructions on their card which were as follows:

Card A: Take as many matches as you currently have.
Card B: Take twice as many matches as you currently have.
Card C: Take four times as many matches as you currently have.

The number of matches remaining for each choice are shown in the table below.

1st volunteer	2nd volunteer	3rd volunteer	Matches taken	Remainder
A	B	C	$1 \times 1 + 2 \times 2 + 4 \times 3 = 17$	$18 - 17 = 1$
B	A	C	$2 \times 1 + 1 \times 2 + 4 \times 3 = 16$	$18 - 16 = 2$
A	C	B	$1 \times 1 + 4 \times 2 + 2 \times 3 = 15$	$18 - 15 = 3$
B	C	A	$2 \times 1 + 4 \times 2 + 1 \times 3 = 13$	$18 - 13 = 5$
C	A	B	$4 \times 1 + 1 \times 2 + 2 \times 3 = 12$	$18 - 12 = 6$
C	B	A	$4 \times 1 + 2 \times 2 + 1 \times 3 = 11$	$18 - 11 = 7$

As can be seen, the given arrangements do give the remainders in the stated order. In his book "Mathematics, Magic and Mystery", Martin Gardner (Gardner (1956)) mentions this trick and suggests using mnemonics to remember the order of the letters in the table. For the given case, using A, B and C as the cards, he suggests the phrase "ABie's BAnk ACcount soon BeComes CAsh CluB", where the two indicated letters represent the letters taken by the first and second volunteer respectively with the letter taken by the third volunteer being the letter not included in the word and the position of the appropriate word within the phrase represents the number of matches remaining. If you like this idea, you may be able to think of a more relevant phrase than this to help you remember how the order of the choices made relate to the number of matches remaining.

Number Trick C11

Choices (2)

The mathematics involved in this trick is a little more involved than that in the previous trick because of the seemingly free choice of the numbers being multiplied. It should be noted, however, that the values on each of the cards do have something in common.

Card A: 17, 24, 10, 38, 52   all of the form $7a + 3$
Card B: 15, 22, 43, 50, 36   all of the form $7b + 1$
Card C: 21, 35, 63, 42, 14   all of the form $7c$

Let the numbers chosen by the first, second and third volunteers be X, Y and Z respectively from the cards numbered 0, 1 and 2.

The first volunteer chooses a number from Card A to multiply their value by, the second chooses a number from Card B to multiply their value by and the third chooses a number from Card C to multiply their number by before their three answers are added to give a final total.

$$\text{Total} = X(7a + 3) + Y(7b + 1) + Z(7c)$$
$$\therefore \text{Total} = 3X + Y + 7(Xa + Yb + Zc)$$

When this total is divided by 7, the remainder will be $3X + Y \pmod 7$. As X, Y and Z take some arrangement of the values 0, 1 and 2, the value $3X + Y$ can take will vary as shown in the table below.

X	Y	Z	3X + Y
0	1	2	1
0	2	1	2
1	0	2	3
1	2	0	5
2	0	1	6
2	1	0	7 $\Rightarrow$ remainder 0

As can be seen, the values of the function $3X + Y$ and hence the values of the remainder are distinct and correspond to the different choice of cards indicated.

172

Number Trick C12

Mind Reading Cards

The idea behind this trick is binary arithmetic. This is where a number is expressed as the sum of powers of 2 rather than as the sum of combinations of powers of 10 as is the case for our usual decimal or base 10 system of numbering.

For example: In base 10 $\quad 37 = 3 \times 10^1 + 7$.

However, the same number in binary or base 2 would be written

$$100101 = 1 \times 2^5 + 0 \times 2^4 + 0 \times 2^3 + 1 \times 2^2 + 0 \times 2^1 + 1.$$

To see why the trick works, every number between 1 and 63 must first be expressed in binary form as shown below.

Number	Binary	Number	Binary	Number	Binary
1	1	22	10110	43	101011
2	10	23	10111	44	101100
3	11	24	11000	45	101101
4	100	25	11001	46	101110
5	101	26	11010	47	101111
6	110	27	11011	48	110000
7	111	28	11100	49	110001
8	1000	29	11101	50	110010
9	1001	30	11110	51	110011
10	1010	31	11111	52	110100
11	1011	32	100000	53	110101
12	1100	33	100001	54	110110
13	1101	34	100010	55	110111
14	1110	35	100011	56	111000
15	1111	36	100100	57	111001
16	10000	37	100101	58	111010
17	10001	38	100110	59	111011
18	10010	39	100111	60	111100
19	10011	40	101000	61	111101
20	10100	41	101001	62	111110
21	10101	42	101010	63	111111

The numbers on card A are then precisely those numbers whose binary form ends in 1 and the numbers on card B are precisely those whose binary form has a 1 as their penultimate digit etc. Thus a number that appears on cards A, C, D and F, as is the case in the example in the description of how to use the trick, will have the form 101101 and so be equal to $1 \times 2^5 + 0 \times 2^4 + 1 \times 2^3 + 1 \times 2^2 + 0 \times 2^1 + 1 = 32 + 8 + 4 + 1 = 45$ as required.

Part D

Miscellaneous Tricks

Number Trick D1

Pascal's Trick (1)

Let the 6-digit number have digits a, b, c, d, e and f.

In the proof of this trick, the initial working will not take into account the part of the problem where only the units digit is written down but will work with the full number. This will not alter the final answer as the timing of when any tens are subtracted is not relevant. Consider the arrangement below where the expressions in each row are formed by adding two adjacent expressions from the previous row in the same way as adjacent digits are added in the numerical problem.

$$a \qquad b \qquad c \qquad d \qquad e \qquad f$$
$$a + b \qquad b + c \qquad c + d \qquad d + e \qquad e + f$$
$$a + 2b + c \qquad b + 2c + d \qquad c + 2d + e \qquad d + 2e + f$$
$$a + 3b + 3c + d \qquad b + 3c + 3d + 3e \qquad c + 3d + 3e + f$$
$$a + 4b + 6c + 4d + e \qquad b + 4c + 6d + 4e + f$$
$$a + 5b + 10c + 10d + 5e + f$$

The algebraic formula for the final result, including any tens, is given by the final line. To show why only certain digits need to be considered when predicting the final result once these tens have been removed, re-write this line in the following way.

$$T = a + f + 5b + 5e + 10c + 10d$$
$$\therefore T = a + f + 5(b + e) + 10(c + d)$$

Now consider the individual parts in turn. Whatever the values of c and d, the term $10(c + d)$ will always be a multiple of 10 and so will have no effect on the units digit of the answer. In a similar way, if $b + e$ is an even number, $5(b + e)$ will also be a multiple of 10 and so will make no contribution to the units digit of the answer. This will be the case if both b and e are even or if both are odd. If, however, one of b and e is even and one is odd, their sum will be an odd number and so can be written in the form $2n + 1$ for some integer n. Calculating $5(2n + 1) = 10n + 5$ shows that this term will then make a contribution of 5 to the units digit of the final answer.

Combining all this information tells us that
   a) If the numbers represented by b and e are of the same parity, the final figure will be the units digit of a + e.
   b) If numbers represented by b and e are of different parity, the final figure will be the units digit of a + e + 5.

Using these results allows the prediction of the final figure after the number is reduced in the way described to be made instantly.

Pascal's Trick (2)

In this trick, the number is reduced by subtracting 9 from any sum that is 9 or more. This, in effect, is the same as asking what the remainder is when the sum is divided by 9 and so the final term from the algebraic consideration will be considered in that same manner. Again the reduction in the algebraic consideration is only considered to take place at the end of the problem. Here the working is turned sideways to ensure the full table will fit on the page.

a	b	c	d	e	f	g	h	i	j
a									
a+b	b								
a+2b+c	b+c	c							
a+3b+3c+d	b+2c+d	c+d	d						
a+4b+6c+4d+e	b+3c+3d+e	c+2d+e	d+e	e					
a+5b+10c+10d+5e+f	b+4c+6d+4e+f	c+3d+3e+f	d+2e+f	e+f	f				
a+6b+15c+20d+15e+6f+g	b+5c+10d+10e+5f+g	c+4d+6e+4f+g	d+3e+3f+g	e+2f+g	f+g	g			
a+7b+21c+35d+35e+21f+7g+h	b+6c+15d+20e+15f+6g+h	c+5d+10e+10f+5g+h	d+4e+6f+4g+h	e+3f+3g+h	f+2g+h	g+h	h		
a+8b+28c+56d+70e+56f+28g+8h+i	b+7c+21d+35e+35f+21g+7h+i	c+6d+15e+20f+15g+6h+i	d+5e+10f+10g+5h+i	e+4f+6g+4h+i	f+3g+3h+i	g+2h+i	h+i	i	
a + 9b + 36c + 84d + 126e + 126f + 84g + 36h + 9i + j	b+8c+28d+56e+70f+56g+28h+8i+j	c+7d+21e+35f+35g+21h+7i+j	d+6e+15f+20g+15h+6i+j	e+5f+10g+10h+5i+j	f+4g+6h+4i+j	g+3h+3i+j	h+2i+j	i+j	j

The final line is of the form

$$T = a + 9b + 36c + 84d + 126e + 126f + 84g + 36h + 9i + j$$

which can be re-written as

$$T = a + j + 84d + 84g + 9b + 36c + 126e + 126f + 36f + 9i$$

or

$$T = a + j + 84d + 84g + 9 \times (b + 4c + 14e + 14f + 4f + i)$$

Only the first four terms of this version of the final line are not divisible by 9 and so only the first four terms will make any contribution to the final value when multiples of 9 are subtracted from the sums at each stage if any sum is 9 or more. However, these four terms can be simplified further by noting that

$$a + j + 84d + 84g = a + j + 3d + 9 \times 9d + 3g + 9 \times 9g$$

and so the terms involving 84d and 84g can be reduced by subtracting multiples of 9 to give 3d and 3g. Thus, to find the value that will appear on the final line after all multiples of 9 have been reduced, one need only consider $a + j + 3(d + g)$ as stated and then subtract any possible multiples of 9 from that to obtain the final result.

178

Number Trick D3

Faster Than A Calculator!

Versions 1 and 2

To demonstrate mathematically why these tricks work, let the two initial numbers chosen be X and Y.

Term	Sequence	Sum up to that term	
1st	X	X	
2nd	Y	X + Y	
3rd	X + Y	2X + 2Y	
4th	X + 2Y	3X + 4Y	
5th	**2X + 3Y**	5X + 7Y	
6th	3X + 5Y	8X + 12Y	$= 4 \times$ (**2X + 3Y**)
7th	**5X + 8Y**	13X + 20Y	
8th	8X + 13Y	21X + 33Y	
9th	13X + 21Y	34X + 54Y	
10th	21X + 34Y	55X + 88Y	$= 11 \times$ (**5X + 8Y**)

As can be seen, whatever values of X and Y are chosen, the sum of the first ten terms of the sequence is equal to 11 times the 7th term and the sum of the first six terms is equal to four times the 5th term.

Version 3

This version will be demonstrated in a very similar way except that the first three terms of the sequence are freely chosen and so will be represented by X, Y and Z.

Term	Sequence	Sum up to that term	
1st	X	X	
2nd	Y	X + Y	
3rd	Z	X + Y + Z	
4th	X + Y + Z	2X + 2Y + 2Z	
5th	X + 2Y + 2Z	3X + 4Y + 4Z	
6th	2X + 3Y + 4Z	5X + 7Y + 8Z	
7th	**4X + 6Y + 7Z**	9X + 13Y + 15Z	
8th	7X + 11Y + 13Z	16X + 24Y + 28Z	$= 4 \times$ (**4X + 6Y + 7Z**)

Again it can be clearly seen that the sum of the first eight terms of this sequence is equal to four times the 7th term as required.

Number Trick D4　　　　**The Choice Is Yours**

If you examine the numbers in the five sets carefully, it can be seen that the numbers in the same set are all closely related.

> Set A: 179 278 773 872 971 377
> Set B: 840 642 543 147 345 741
> Set C: 483 681 285 384 780 186
> Set D: 762 564 960 366 168 663
> Set E: 558 459 855 657 756 954

The central number in each set is always the same (7 for set A, 4 for set B, 8 for set C, 6 for set D and 5 for set E) and the outer two digits for all the numbers in each set add up to the same value (10 for set A, 8 for set B, 7 for set C, 9 for set D and 13 for set E). Thus a general formula can be written for the numbers of each set that depends only on the final digit of the number.

Let the final digits of the numbers chosen from sets A, B, C, D and E be a, b, c, d and e respectively. The formulae for the numbers in each set are then as follows:

Set A: $(10 - a) \times 100 + 70 + a$
Set B: $(8 - b) \times 100 + 40 + b$
Set A: $(7 - c) \times 100 + 80 + c$
Set A: $(9 - d) \times 100 + 60 + d$
Set A: $(13 - e) \times 100 + 50 + e$

Thus if a number is chosen at random from each set and then the five numbers added, the sum S will be given by the formula

$$S = (10 - a) \times 100 + 70 + a + (8 - b) \times 100 + 40 + b + (7 - c) \times 100 + 80 + c$$
$$+ (9 - d) \times 100 + 60 + d + (13 - e) \times 100 + 50 + e$$

$$\therefore S = (10 + 8 + 7 + 9 + 13 - a - b - c - d - e) \times 100 + 300 + a + b + c + d + e$$

$$\therefore S = (47 - (a + b + c + d + e)) \times 100 + 300 + a + b + c + d + e$$

$$\therefore S = (50 - (a + b + c + d + e)) \times 100 + (a + b + c + d + e)$$

Thus if you add up the unit digits of the numbers selected, this will give you the final two digits of the sum and subtracting this answer from 50 will give you the first two digits of the sum.

It is quite straightforward to invent similar problems along the same lines with different quantities of sets of numbers or numbers within each set involved provided the common values in the centre of the 3-digit numbers for each set add up to a multiple of 10. This is to ensure that they do not contribute to the value in the final two digits of the answer. A second example of this type of trick using only three sets and four numbers within each set is given below.

Set 1: 775 676 379 874   general term $(12 - x) \times 100 + 70 + x$
Set 2: 580 481 283 382   general term $(5 - y) \times 100 + 80 + y$
Set 3: 655 853 259 457   general term $(11 - z) \times 100 + 50 + z$

$$\text{Sum } S = (28 - (x + y + z)) \times 100 + 200 + x + y + z$$
$$\text{or} \quad S = (30 - (x + y + z)) \times 100 + x + y + z$$

To obtain the solution for this set of numbers if one number from each set is chosen and then these chosen numbers added together, add the units digits of the numbers chosen to get the final two digits of the sum and subtract this answer from 30 to get the first two (or one) digits (or digit) of the sum.

Number Trick D5

Rectangular Adding

The proof for the working of this trick will come in two parts. First I will show that the specific trick demonstrated works on a 100 square and then I will extend the proof to the more general situation.

Consider the following 4×5 rectangle of squares taken from a 100 square. Let the value in the top left hand corner be n.

n	n + 1	n + 2	n + 3	n + 4
n + 10	n + 11	n + 12	n + 13	n + 14
n + 20	n + 21	n + 22	n + 23	n + 24
n + 30	n + 31	n + 32	n + 33	n + 34

The sum of these values is $20n + 340 = 10 \times (2n + 34) = 10 \times (n + n + 34)$. But the values n and n + 34 are precisely those in the top left and bottom right squares of the rectangle and so the trick does work as described.

Now let us consider the more general case. Let the increases moving one square horizontally across the number grid and one square vertically down the number grid be x and y respectively and let the size of the rectangle to be drawn on the grid be $p \times q$. Let the value in the top left hand square of the rectangle be n. The general formula for the sum of each row of the rectangle is included in the table below to aid with the algebraic simplification.

						Sum of row
n	n + a	n + 2a	n + 3a	...	n + (q − 1)a	qn + a(q − 1)q/2
n + b	n + b + a	n + b + 2a	n + b + 3a	...	n + b + (q − 1)a	qn + a(q − 1)q/2 + qb
n + 2b	n + 2b + a	n + 2b + 2a	n + 2b + 3a	...	n + 2b + (q − 1)a	qn + a(q − 1)q/2 + 2qb
n + (p − 1)b	n + (p − 1)b + a	n + (p − 1)b + 2a	n + (p − 1)b + 3a	...	n + (p − 1)b + (q − 1)a	qn + a(q − 1)q/2 + (p − 1)qb

The sum of all the values in the rectangle is given by the sum of all the rows, namely

$$S = qn + a(q - 1)q/2 + qn + a(q - 1)q/2 + qb + qn + a(q - 1)q/2 + 2qb + \ldots + qn + a(q - 1)q/2 + (p - 1)qb$$

$$\therefore S = p \times qn + p \times q \times (q - 1)a/2 + qb \times (1 + 2 + \ldots + (p - 1))$$

$$\therefore S = p \times qn + p \times q \times (q - 1)a/2 + qb \times (p - 1)p/2$$

$$\therefore S = \tfrac{1}{2} \times p \times q \times (2n + (q - 1)a + (p - 1)b)$$
$$\text{or}$$
$$\therefore S = \tfrac{1}{2} \times p \times q \times (n + (n + (q - 1)a + (p - 1)b))$$

As the formulae for the values in the top left square and the bottom right square of the rectangle are n and n + (p − 1)b + (q − 1)a respectively, the sum of all the values in the rectangle is equal to = ½ × (number of values in the rectangle) × (top left value + bottom right value) as stated. That the alternative formula is also true is easily seen by observing that the formulae in the top right square and bottom left square are n +

(q − 1)a and n + (p − 1)b respectively and these formulae have the same sum as the formulae from the top left and bottom right squares.

Number Trick D6

Multiples (1)

This trick is illustrating the fact that if $1000X + a$ is a multiple of 11 (or 13) where X and a are whole numbers between 1 and 999 inclusive, then $1000a + X$ will also be a multiple of 11 (or 13).

I will consider the version involving divisibility by 11 first.

If $1000X + a$ is a multiple of 11 then
$$1000X + a = 11k \qquad \text{for some integer } k$$
$$\therefore 90 \times 11X + 10X + a = 11k$$
$$\therefore 10X + a = 11k - 90 \times 11X$$
$$\therefore 10X + a = 11 \times (k - 90X)$$
$$\therefore a = 11 \times (k - 90X) - 10X$$
$$\therefore 10a = 11 \times (k - 90X) \times 10 - 100X$$
$$\therefore 10a = 11 \times (k - 90X) \times 10 - 9 \times 11X - X$$

Now consider $1000a + X$
$$1000a + X = 90 \times 11a + 10a + X$$
$$\therefore 1000a + X = 90 \times 11a + 11 \times (k - 90X) \times 10 - 9 \times 11X - X + X$$
$$\therefore 1000a + X = 90 \times 11a + 11 \times (k - 90X) \times 10 - 9 \times 11X$$
$$\therefore 1000a + X = 11 \times (90a + (k - 90X) \times 10 - 9X)$$

i.e. $1000a + X$ is a multiple of 11.

The version involving divisibility by 13 follows in a very similar way as shown below.

If $1000X + a$ is a multiple of 13 then
$$1000X + a = 13m \qquad \text{for some integer } m$$
$$\therefore 76 \times 13X + 12X + a = 13m$$
$$\therefore 12X + a = 13m - 76 \times 13X$$
$$\therefore 12X + a = 13 \times (m - 76X)$$
$$\therefore a = 13 \times (m - 76X) - 12X$$
$$\therefore 12a = 13 \times (m - 76X) \times 12 - 144X$$
$$\therefore 12a = 13 \times (m - 76X) \times 12 - 11 \times 13X - X$$

Now consider $1000a + X$
$$1000a + X = 76 \times 13a + 12a + X$$
$$\therefore 1000a + X = 76 \times 13a + 13 \times (m - 76X) \times 12 - 11 \times 13X - X + X$$
$$\therefore 1000a + X = 76 \times 13a + 13 \times (m - 76X) \times 12 - 11 \times 13X$$
$$\therefore 1000a + X = 13 \times (76a + (m - 76X) \times 12 - 11X)$$

i.e. $1000a + X$ is a multiple of 13.

In fact a similar argument can also be applied to show that, if $1000X + a$ is a multiple of 7, then $1000a + X$ will also be a multiple of 7.

Number Trick D7

Multiples (2)

The key points used in proving why this trick works are that 111 and hence 999 are multiples of 37 ($111 = 3 \times 37$, $999 = 27 \times 37$).

Let the 3-digit number called out be abc ($= 100 \times a + 10 \times b + c$)

Consider the 6-digit number abc,def

$$\text{abc,def} = 1000 \times (100 \times a + 10 \times b + c) + (100 \times d + 10 \times e + f)$$

$$\therefore \text{abc,def} = 999 \times (100 \times a + 10 \times b + c) + (100 \times a + 10 \times b + c) + (100 \times d + 10 \times e + f)$$

$$\therefore \text{abc,def} = 27 \times 37 \times (100 \times a + 10 \times b + c) + (100 \times (a + d) + 10 \times (b + e) + (c + f))$$

If $a + d = b + e = c + f = k$ (say), then

$$\therefore \text{abc,def} = 27 \times 37 \times (100 \times a + 10 \times b + c) + (100 \times k + 10 \times k + k)$$

$$\therefore \text{abc,def} = 27 \times 37 \times (100 \times a + 10 \times b + c) + 111 \times k$$

$$\therefore \text{abc,def} = 27 \times 37 \times (100 \times a + 10 \times b + c) + 3 \times 37 \times k$$

$$\therefore \text{abc,def} = 37 \times (27 \times (100 \times a + 10 \times b + c) + 3 \times k)$$

i.e. if $a + d = b + e = c + f$, then abc,def is a multiple of 37.

The proof that the 6-digit number def,abc will be a multiple of 37 under the same conditions follows in exactly the same way.

Consider the 9-digit number pqr,abc,stu.

$$\text{pqr,abc,stu} = 1000000 \times (100 \times p + 10 \times q + r) + 1000 \times (100 \times a + 10 \times b + c) + (100 \times s + 10 \times t + u)$$

$$\therefore \text{pqr,abc,stu} = 999999 \times (100 \times p + 10 \times q + r) + (100 \times p + 10 \times q + r) + 999 \times (100 \times a + 10 \times b + c) + (100 \times a + 10 \times b + c) + (100 \times s + 10 \times t + u)$$

$$\therefore \text{pqr,abc,stu} = 27027 \times 37 \times (100 \times p + 10 \times q + r) + 27 \times 37 \times (100 \times a + 10 \times b + c) + (100 \times (p + a + s) + 10 \times (q + b + t) + (r + c + u))$$

If $p + a + s = q + b + t = r + c + u = k$ (say), then

$$\therefore \text{pqr,abc,stu} = 27027 \times 37 \times (100 \times p + 10 \times q + r) + 27 \times 37 \times (100 \times a + 10 \times b + c) + (100 \times k + 10 \times k + k)$$

$\therefore$ pqr,abc,stu = 27027 × 37 × (100 × p + 10 × q + r) + 27 × 37 × (100 × a + 10 × b + c) + 111 × k

$\therefore$ pqr,abc,stu = 27027 × 37 × (100 × p + 10 × q + r) + 27 × 37 × (100 × a + 10 × b + c) + 3 × 37 × k

$\therefore$ pqr,abc,stu = 37 × (27027 × (100 × p + 10 × q + r) + 27 × (100 × a + 10 × b + c) + 3 × k)

i.e. if p + a + s = q + b + t = r + c + u, then pqr,abc,stu is a multiple of 37.

The proof that the other 9-digit numbers pqr,stu,abc and abc,pqr,stu will be multiples of 37 under the same conditions follow in exactly the same way.

Number Trick D8

Matching Matches (1)

Let the initial number of matches be 18X.

Let the number of matches taken by the first volunteer be $10a + b$ where $0 \le b \le 9$.

$\therefore$ The second volunteer will start with $18X - (10a + b)$ matches.

The digit sum of the number of matches taken by the first volunteer is $a + b$.

When the first volunteer gives the second volunteer the number of matches equal to that digit sum, the first volunteer will then have $10a + b - (a + b) = 9a$ matches and the second volunteer will have $18X - (10a + b) + a + b = 18X - 9a$ matches.

These will be equal when

$$9a = 18X - 9a$$
$$\Rightarrow 18a = 18X \text{ or } a = X$$

This tells us that the two volunteers will end up with the same number of matches from a pile of 18X matches when the number taken by the first volunteer is of the form $10X + b$ where $0 \le b \le 9$.

This is precisely the situation you have when you start with 54 ($= 18 \times 3$) matches and tell the first volunteer to take more than 29 but fewer than 40 matches.

Number Trick D9

Matching Matches (2)

Let the number chosen by A be n.

	A	B	C
Initially	4n	7n	13n
C gives away matches	4n + 4n = 8n	7n + 7n = 14n	13n − 4n − 7n = 2n
B gives away matches	8n + 8n = 16n	14n − 8n − 2n = 4n	2n + 2n = 4n
A gives away matches	16n − 4n − 4n = 8n	4n + 4n = 8n	4n + 4n = 8n

From the table, it can be easily seen that, whatever the value of n, all three volunteers will end up with the same number of matches.

Number Trick D10
I Know How Many You Have!

The simplest way to prove why the three versions of this trick work is to consider a table showing the formulae for the number of matches possessed by each person at each stage. In all cases, the number of matches initially placed in any pile will be taken as Y.

Version 1

Let the number of matches moved from pile A to pile B be X.

	Pile A	Pile B	Pile C
Initially	Y	Y	Y
A and C move matches to pile B	Y − X	Y + X + X = Y + 2X	Y − X
Pile C is doubled in size	Y − X	Y + 2X − (Y − X) = 3X	2(Y − X)

It can be seen that the final size of pile B is three times the number you stated should be transferred from each of piles A and C to pile B. Thus, however pile B is split and one portion given to you, you will always know the total number of matches that were in the pile prior to the split and hence be able to work out how many matches have been retained in pile B.

Version 2

Let the number of matches moved from pile A to pile B and from pile D to pile C be X.

	Pile A	Pile B	Pile C	Pile D
Initially	Y	Y	Y	Y
A and D move matches to piles B and C	Y − X	Y + X	Y + X	Y − X
Piles B and C are combined	Y − X	Y + X + Y + X = 2Y + 2X		Y − X
Piles A and D are doubled in size	2(Y − X)	2Y + 2X − (Y − X) − (Y − X) = 4X		2(Y − X)

It can be seen that the final size of the combined pile is four times the number you stated should be transferred from pile A to pile B and from pile D to pile C. Thus, however the combined pile is split and one portion given to you, you will always know the total number of matches that were in the pile prior to the split and hence be able to work out how many matches have been retained in the combined pile.

Version 3

This version is almost identical to the previous case except that different numbers of matches are transferred from pile A and pile D at the start.

Let the number of matches transferred from pile A to pile B be X and let the number of matches transferred from pile D to pile C be Z.

	Pile A	Pile B	Pile C	Pile D
Initially	Y	Y	Y	Y
A and D move matches to piles B and C	$Y - X$	$Y + X$	$Y + Z$	$Y - Z$
Piles B and C are combined	$Y - X$	$Y + X + Y + Z$ $= 2Y + X + Z$		$Y - Z$
Piles A and D are doubled in size	$2(Y - X)$	$2Y + X + Z - (Y - X) - (Y - Z)$ $= 2X + 2Z = 2(X + Z)$		$2(Y - Z)$

It can be seen that the final size of the combined pile is twice the sum of the numbers of matches you stated should be transferred from pile A to pile B and from pile D to pile C. Thus, however the combined pile is split and one portion given to you, you will always know the total number of matches that were in the pile prior to the split and hence be able to work out how many matches have been retained in the combined pile.

Number Trick D11

Magic Square

Because the square below is a magic square with constant zero, it can be used as a base for other magic squares.

−20	1	12	7
11	8	−21	2
5	10	3	−18
4	−19	6	9

The four negative values are arranged within the square so that there is one in each row, one in each column, one on both diagonals, one in each of the corner 2×2 squares and one in the centre 2×2 square. This means that if the same number is added to each of the negative values, the square will remain a magic square with the new constant equal to the number that was added.

Any value (N) can be added to each of the four negative values but
  a) if N > 21, all the values in the square will be positive
  b) if N = 34, all the values from 1 to 16 will appear once and once only
  c) if N ≥ 34, all the values in the square will only occur once

The refinement, which you can use for values of the required magic constant (N) that are both multiples of 4 and satisfy N > 88, is to add N/4 to each of the values in the magic square of constant 0. This will obviously give a magic square with magic constant N, but you will be unable to write down any values for your square in advance of hearing the value of the constant required.

Another interesting mathematical curiosity, related to magic squares is known as an antimagic square. This is where all rows, columns and diagonals add up to different values. An example for a 3×3 square using the digits 1 to 9 is shown below.

5	1	3
4	2	6
8	7	9

Number Trick D12

Magic Spelling

The mathematics involved in creating this trick must have been considerable and so I will not attempt to justify it here. There has been some effort by puzzlers in recent years to find other puzzles with both arithmetic and linguistic properties. One such example of this is to consider actual magic squares which have special properties related to the spelling of the numbers involved. These are known as alphamagic squares and I will illustrate one of these here.

Consider the following 3 × 3 magic square.

5	22	18
28	15	2
12	8	25

Now form a square by writing the words for these values in their own 3 × 3 square.

five	twenty-two	eighteen
twenty-eight	fifteen	two
twelve	eight	twenty-five

Next count the number of letters in the words and use these numbers to form a 3 × 3 square.

4	9	8
11	7	3
6	5	10

This square is itself a magic square, making the first square an alphamagic square. Once you have found one alphamagic square, different squares can be created from it by adding the same value to each entry in the individual cells provided the spelling of the term added also results in an increase of the same number of letters in each case. For example, provided adding 100 to any number under 100 is written in letters as "one hundred and" the original number, then adding 100 to each of the cells in the original square above will also result in an alphamagic square. It is possible to have alphamagic squares in other languages as well. Below is one in German taken from an article in "Science News Online" by Ivars Peterson (Peterson (2003)) although the magic square that results when you count the letters of the words is a little simple as all entries are equal to the same value (14).

fünfundvierzig (45)	zweiundsechzig (62)	achtundfünfzig (58)
achtundsechzig (68)	fünfundfünfzig (55)	zweiundvierzig (42)
zweiundfünfzig (52)	achtundvierzig (48)	fünfundsechzig (65)

Why

The Card
Tricks
Work

Card Trick Mathematics

In this section I will examine the underlying mathematics within the card tricks described earlier. It is the mathematics, rather than any sleight of hand, that causes these tricks to work. This means the tricks can be carried out with only a little preparation, making them suitable for use in the classroom or by any budding magician looking for some simple tricks to get them started. In some cases the maths described will be little more than a numerical demonstration, but in other cases there will be some more complex algebra involved. As I said when describing <u>how</u> the tricks worked, it is not necessary to understand the maths involved to be able to carry out the tricks. However, an understanding of <u>why</u> they are working does allow you to develop variants of your own or, if the tricks are being used in the classroom, allows you to challenge pupils to work out the reasoning for themselves.

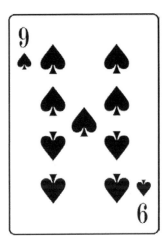

Card Trick 1

A 10 Card Trick

The key to this trick lies in somehow positioning the chosen card as the 5th card down from the top. This is because, for a packet of ten cards, if a card elimination process like the one described in the trick is carried out, it is the 5th card of the packet that will remain at the end.

To demonstrate this, consider the numbers   1 2 3 4 5 6 7 8 9 10

The process used to eliminate cards is equivalent to moving the first to the end of the list, then removing the second, moving the third to the end of the list then removing the fourth etc.

After one run through the list, all the even numbers will have been removed leaving the list 1 3 5 7 9

This time, values 3 and 7 will be eliminated, leaving the list   9 1 5

Then 1 will be eliminated, leaving   5 9   and finally 9 will be eliminated, leaving 5.

To prove that the trick will work, it now remains to show that the process described will place the chosen card as the 5th card down from the top.

Let us assume the number chosen was X.
Thus the initial position of the cards within the packet before you start to move them
is   X – 1 cards
                                    Chosen card
                                    10 – X cards

The way the cards are moved, in groups of one, two or three, does not alter the order in which the cards occur within the packet but only their position in the packet. The number of cards you move is of the form $10n + 5$ and so, as the packet only contains ten cards, this is equivalent to moving only five cards. Therefore, after you have moved your cards, the position of the cards within the packet is as follows:

          X – 6 cards   4 + X cards
          Chosen card   Chosen card
          15 – X cards   5 – X cards

Here the two different possibilities correspond to different choices for the number chosen and are for $X \geq 6$ and $X \leq 5$ respectively. The second position is more complex to obtain because, if $X \leq 5$, you will actually move the chosen card when you move your five cards as illustrated in the table below.

Initial situation			Final situation
X – 1 cards			4 + X cards
Chosen card	Chosen card	9 cards	Chosen card
10 – X cards	9 cards	Chosen card	5 – X cards
Move X – 1 cards	*Move 1 card*	*Move 5 – X cards*	

When they then move X cards from the top to the bottom of the packet, these situations both become

4 cards

Chosen card

5 cards

This is easily seen in the second case but the first case does require a more thorough demonstration. The X cards to be moved are split up into three stages, namely moving X – 6 cards, moving one card and moving five cards to make a total of X cards moved as required. The stages that this process goes though are shown in the table below.

Initial situation			Final situation
X – 6 cards			4 cards
Chosen card	Chosen card	9 cards	Chosen card
15 – X cards	9 cards	Chosen card	5 cards
Move X – 6 cards	*Move 1 card*	*Move 5 cards*	

This makes the chosen card the 5th card from the top of the packet as required and so the elimination process will reveal the chosen card.

Card Trick 2

Can You Find My Card?

The key behind the next two tricks is that, whatever the number of cards, there is a rule that will allow you to work out which card will remain after the rest are eliminated for this type of dealing.

For card elimination using the under/down method, where the first card is moved form the top of the packet to the bottom and the next card discarded etc, the rule is as follows:

- Subtract the largest power of 2 you can from the number of cards in the packet
- Double your answer
- Add 1

This will give the position of the card in the face-down packet that will be retained.

Mathematically, this is equivalent to saying that if the packet contains n cards and $2^m \leq n < 2^{m+1}$, then the retained card has position $r = 2 \times (n - 2^m) + 1$.

An alternative way of finding the position of the card was mentioned by Martin Gardner in his book "The Unexpected Hanging and Other Mathematical Diversions" (Gardner (1991)), and credited to Nathan Mendelsohn. This requires the number of cards to be written in binary form.

$$n = 1y...cba = 1 \times 2^m + y \times 2^{m-1} + ... + c \times 2^2 + b \times 2^1 + a$$

where a, b, c … y are all either 0 or 1.

The initial 1 is then removed from the front of the number and placed at the end to give the position of the retained card in binary form.

$$r = y...cba1 = y \times 2^m + ... + c \times 2^3 + b \times 2^2 + a \times 2^1 + 1.$$

If the down/under method of dealing is used where the first card is discarded and the next moved from the top of the packet to the bottom etc, the rule is very similar except that in the case of the formula, the "+ 1" term is not required, and in the case of the binary method, it is a 0 that is placed at the end after the initial 1 is removed from the front of the binary number.

In this case, the first card is moved to the bottom and the second card discarded and so on and, as the number of cards involved are all in the range $16 < n < 32$, the required formula to calculate the position of the card that will remain is $2 \times (n - 16) + 1$.

Card Trick 3

A Down-Under Trick

Let the number of cards taken by the volunteer be X (< 16).

This means that the card they remember will be the Xth card from the bottom of the packet of 16 cards dealt face-up. When this packet is turned over, the remembered card will then be the Xth card from the top. Adding the X removed cards on top means that the remembered card is now the $2X^{th}$ card in a packet of $16 + X$ cards.

Using the formula for down/under dealing described in Card Trick 2, the remaining card in a packet of $16 + X$ cards where $X < 16$ will have the position

$$r = 2 \times (16 + X - 16) = 2X$$

This means that the card they remembered will be the one remaining.

Card Trick 4

A Confusing Card Trick

The mathematics behind this seemingly intricate trick is remarkably simple. All you are really doing is putting the chosen cards in the positions that will remain when the remaining cards are eliminated. The initial set-up leaves the chosen cards as the 38th, 22nd and 6th cards from the top of the face-down pack respectively. This occurs because the cutting of cards to hide the chosen card is irrelevant to its final position once the cards have been gathered in the manner described. The table below shows that, if the cards are dealt as described, namely alternately face-up and face down, starting with the face-up pile first and, once all the cards have been dealt, continuing the process with the face-down pile each time, it will be the 38th, 22nd and 6th cards that are isolated. The numbers in the table represent the position of the cards from the top of the face-down pile just prior to the first card of the elimination process being dealt.

	First	Deal	Second	Deal	Third	Deal	Fourth	Deal
	Face-up	Face-down	Face-up	Face-down	Face-up	Face-down	Face-up	Face-down
Top	1	2	52	50	2	**6**	46	**38**
	3	4	48	46	10	14	30	**22**
	5	**6**	44	42	18	**22**	14	**6**
	7	8	40	**38**	26	30		
	9	10	36	34	34	**38**		
	11	12	32	30	42	46		
	13	14	28	26	50			
	15	16	24	**22**				
	17	18	20	18				
	19	20	16	14				
	21	**22**	12	10				
	23	24	8	**6**				
	25	26	4	2				
	27	28						
	29	30						
	31	32						
	33	34						
	35	36						
	37	**38**						
	39	40						
	41	42						
	43	44						
	45	46						
	47	48						
	49	50						
Bottom	51	52						

The alternate method works in a very similar way. However, in that case, the chosen cards become the 42nd, 26th and 10th cards from the top of the face-down packet when the four cards are moved from the bottom to the top and these in turn become the 11th, 27th and 43rd cards from the top of the face-up packet once the packet is turned over. Isolating three cards by dealing cards alternately face-up and face-down, starting with the face-up card each time and then retaining the face-up pile until the final step when the three cards from the face-down pile are chosen leaves the three required cards as the next table shows. Here the card number represents its position from the top of the face-up pile just before the first card is dealt in the elimination process.

	First Deal		Second Deal		Third Deal		Fourth Deal	
	Face-up	Face-down	Face-up	Face-down	Face-up	Face-down	Face-up	Face-down
Top	1	2	51	49	3	**7**	51	**43**
	3	4	47	45	**11**	15	35	**27**
	5	6	**43**	41	19	23	19	**11**
	7	8	39	37	**27**	31	3	
	9	10	35	33	35	39		
	11	12	31	29	**43**	47		
	13	14	**27**	25	51			
	15	16	23	21				
	17	18	19	17				
	19	20	15	13				
	21	22	**11**	9				
	23	24	7	5				
	25	26	3	1				
	27	28						
	29	30						
	31	32						
	33	34						
	35	36						
	37	38						
	39	40						
	41	42						
	43	44						
	45	46						
	47	48						
	49	50						
Bottom	51	52						

Card Trick 5

A More Confusing Card Trick

This trick works in a very similar way to the previous trick, although it is quicker to perform as only two sets of dealing into piles are required to isolate the chosen cards. The cutting of piles to hide the chosen cards actually has no effect when the piles are gathered in the way described, meaning the chosen cards are the 51st, 35th, 19th and 3rd cards from the top of the face-down pack. These are precisely the cards isolated when the cards are dealt into four piles, the third pile chosen and then dealt into four piles again, with the first pile being chosen on the second occasion as it is the only one containing four cards. The table below shows that this process does indeed isolate the desired cards with the numbers representing the position of the card in the face-down pile prior to the first card of the elimination process being dealt.

Pile	First	Deal			Second	Deal		
	1	**2**	**3**	**4**	**1**	**2**	**3**	**4**
	1	2	**3**	4	**51**	47	43	39
	5	6	7	8	**35**	31	27	23
	9	10	11	12	**19**	15	11	7
	13	14	15	16	**3**			
	17	18	**19**	20				
	21	22	23	24				
	25	26	27	28				
	29	30	31	32				
	33	34	**35**	36				
	37	38	39	40				
	41	42	43	44				
	45	46	47	48				
	49	50	**51**	52				

Card Trick 6

And The Missing Card Is

This trick is actually one of my own concoctions, although it is easy to see where the different parts have come from. The key to the trick is to get the required card to position 22 because this is the card that will remain when the other cards are eliminated using the type of deal described. This is done in a similar way to that used in Card Trick 27 by Michael Smith.

Let the number chosen be N.

If N cards are then dealt, the number remaining in your hand will be $52 - N$.

When 32 cards are dealt face-up, the number remaining in hand will then be $52 - N - 32 = 20 - N$. The memorised card needs to be in position 22 to be the card that remains when the remaining pack is eliminated, as will be shown below. This means the card remembered must lie $22 - (20 - N) = 2 + N$ cards down the packet of 32 cards dealt.

The table below shows that it is indeed the 22nd and hence the remembered card that remains when the other cards are eliminated.

	1st Deal		2nd Deal		3rd Deal		4th Deal		5th Deal	
Top	Face-up	Face-down	Face-up	Face-down	Face-up	Face-down	Face-up	Face-down	Face-up	Face-down
	1	2	52	50	2	6	46	38	6	**22**
	3	4	48	46	10	14	30	**22**	38	
	5	6	44	42	18	**22**	14	6		
	7	8	40	38	26	30				
	9	10	36	34	34	38				
	11	12	32	30	42	46				
	13	14	28	26	50					
	15	16	24	**22**						
	17	18	20	18						
	19	20	16	14						
	21	**22**	12	10						
	23	24	8	6						
	25	26	4	2						
	27	28								
	29	30								
	31	32								
	33	34								
	35	36								
	37	38								
	39	40								
	41	42								
	43	44								
	45	46								
	47	48								
	49	50								
Bottom	51	52								

Card Trick 7

A Rather Simple Trick

For this trick to work in the way described initially, the number of cards cut must be between 20 and 29 inclusive.

Let the number of cards cut be $20 + X$.

If $0 \leq X \leq 9$ then the digit sum will be $2 + X$.

The card looked at will then be $X + 2$ cards from the bottom of the pile (where the first card from the bottom is taken to be the bottom card itself), meaning that the chosen card will have $20 + X - (2 + X) = 18$ cards above it.

Spelling out the phrase *a rather simple trick*, which has 18 letters, will use these 18 cards leaving the chosen card as the next card in the pile.

If it seems that the number of cards cut was between 30 and 39, then the following refinement is required.

Let the number of cards cut be $30 + Y$.

This number will have digit sum $3 + Y$ provided $0 \leq Y \leq 9$.

The card looked at will then be $Y + 3$ cards from the bottom of the pile and so will have $30 + Y - (3 + Y) = 27$ cards above it.

The alternative phrase *a rather simple trick to perform*, which has 27 letters, uses up these cards leaving the next card as the card chosen.

Card Trick 8

And One For Luck!

For this trick to work, the number of cards cut must be between 10 and 19 inclusive.

Let the number of cards cut be $10 + X$ for $0 \leq X \leq 9$.

One card will be discarded into the first pile and X cards discarded into the second pile. This will leave the volunteer with $10 + X - (X + 1) = 9$ cards in hand and so the chosen card will be the 9th card from the top of the face-down pile when the packet in hand is replaced on top of the unused cards.

Moving the first "one for luck" card from the top to the bottom of the pile will then make the chosen card the 8th card from the top.

Let the number called out be $10 + Y$ where $0 \leq Y \leq 9$.
Dealing $10 + Y$ cards face-down will leave the chosen card as the 8th from the bottom and so will have $10 + Y - 8 = 2 + Y$ cards above it.

The digit sum of the number called out is $1 + Y$ and so discarding this many cards leaves us with only one card above the chosen card.

When the second "one for luck" card is discarded, the chosen card will then be the top card of the packet and so can be revealed.

Card Trick 9

Mind Reader

Let the number of cards cut be 20 + X.

If $0 \leq X \leq 9$, the digit sum will be 2 + X.

Discarding this many cards will then leave $20 + X - (X + 2) = 18$ cards in their hand.

Let the number chosen be Y. If Y cards are discarded, then the number of cards remaining will be 18 − Y with the chosen card being the Yth card in the packet.

Listing and counting the cards read out then tells you the value of 18 − Y.
If you calculate $18 - (18 - Y) = Y$, you will then know the value chosen and hence, by checking the card that is that many down your list, you will be able to reveal the card remembered.

In the instance that more than 18 cards are read out, the analysis above will not hold because more than 29 cards will have been cut initially. If that is the case, the maths involved is very similar except 30 replaces 20 and 27 replaces 18 in the analysis.

Let the number of cards cut be 30 + X.

If $0 \leq X \leq 9$, the digit sum will be 3 + X.

Discarding this many cards will then leave $30 + X - (X + 3) = 27$ cards in their hand.

Let the number chosen be Y. If Y cards are discarded, then the number of cards remaining will be 27 − Y with the chosen card being the Yth card in the packet.

Listing and counting the cards read out tells you the value of 27 − Y.
If you calculate $27 - (27 - Y) = Y$, you will then know the value chosen and hence, by checking the card that is that many down your list, you will be able to reveal the card remembered.

Card Trick 10

It's All In The Cut

This trick is a more sensitive one in terms of the number of cards that must be in the "half" of the pack when it is cut. For the trick to work as described, the chosen card needs to be in the middle of the pile of 13 that is identified.

Let the part chosen contain $24 + X$ cards.

When the pack is reformed, the chosen card will have $28 - X$ cards on top of it.

As mentioned above, for the trick to work, the chosen card will need to be in the middle of the pile of 13 cards it is dealt into i.e. be the 7th card in that pile. This means that the chosen card must have been the 25th, 26th, 27th or 28th card dealt and so there must have been between 24 and 27 cards above the chosen card in the reformed pack.

$$\therefore 24 \leq 28 - X \leq 27 \Rightarrow 1 \leq X \leq 4.$$

Hence the number of cards in the chosen part of the pack must have had between 25 and 28 cards inclusive in it.

As the chosen card is the 7th card in its pile, when this pile is re-dealt into four piles, it will be the middle card in the third pile. When you pick up the middle pile first, the chosen card will be the 2nd card from the top of the packet and, using the formula for down-under dealing described in Card Trick 2, it is the $2 \times (9 - 8) = 2^{nd}$ card in a packet of nine that will remain when the rest are eliminated in the manner described as shown below.

Consider starting with	1 2 3 4 5 6 7 8 9
The first run through the cards leaves	9 2 4 6 8
The next run through leaves	8 2 4
Then	4 2
And finally	2

In these lists, each time it is the first card that is discarded, then the next card moved to the bottom etc.

Card Trick 11

To Lie Or Not To Lie?

The key to this trick is in the initial positioning of the chosen card as the third card down from the top of the packet as, from that initial position, the position of the chosen card after each stage of the trick is always the same, no matter what card is spelt out.

When the value of the card is spelt out, the word used will either have three letters (Ace, two, six, ten), four letters (four, five, nine, Jack, King) or five letters (three, seven, eight, Queen). This means that the chosen card, as the third card down from the top, will always be dealt and will always have two cards beneath it together with no, one or two cards dealt on top. When this dealt packet is replaced at the bottom of the original packet of nine cards, the chosen card will, therefore, always have two cards beneath it and so be the seventh card down from the top.

The effect of spelling out the word *of* will always be to move two cards from the top to the bottom of the packet, making the chosen card the fifth card down from the top.

When the suit of the card is spelt out, the word used will either have five letters (clubs), six letters (hearts, spades) or eight letters (diamonds). This means that the chosen card will, again, always be dealt and will always have four cards beneath it together with no, one or three cards on top of it. When this dealt packet is replaced at the bottom of the original packet, the chosen card will again be the fifth card from the top.

Spelling out any five letter word, such as the suggested word *magic*, and revealing the final card, will always produce the chosen card.

Card Trick 12

A Spelling Trick

Let the number chosen be X, meaning that a packet of X cards is removed.

The remembered card will then be the Xth card in the remaining face-down pack and so have $X - 1$ cards above it.

Let the name of the person have Y letters.

When you spell out their name, you will deal Y cards, face-down, into a pile which will mean that the remembered card is now the Xth card from the bottom of the pack with $Y - X$ cards above it.

If this pile is then placed on top of the remaining cards and the removed packet placed on top of that, there will be $Y - X + X = Y$ cards on top of the remembered card. Asking your volunteer to spell out their name will use up these Y cards, making the remembered card the new top card of the pile.

The restriction that the name of the volunteer has to have more than ten letters in it is to ensure that the quantity $Y - X$ is positive.

Card Trick 13

The World's Greatest Magician

Let the number of cards removed be X.

When the 20 cards are dealt face-up on the table, the card remembered will be the Xth card and will have $X - 1$ cards below it and $20 - X$ cards above it.

The remaining pack will contain $52 - X - 20 = 32 - X$ cards.

When the 20-card packet is turned over and placed at the bottom of the remaining pack, the remembered card will then have $32 - X + X - 1 = 31$ cards above it.

Dealing one card per letter while spelling out the phrase _who is the world's greatest magician_, which has 30 letters plus one extra card to be dealt for the apostrophe, will use up these 31 cards, leaving the next card as the card remembered.

Card Trick 14
I Wish All My Card Tricks Worked This Easily

Let the number chosen be X.

The initial position after the packet of cards is removed and the card is chosen is as follows:

$$X - 1 \text{ cards}$$
$$\text{Chosen card}$$
$$52 - 2X \text{ cards}$$

Dealing 15 cards into a face-up pile on the table, leaves the following situation:

face-up	face-down
$15 - X$ cards	$37 - X$ cards
Chosen card	
$X - 1$ cards	

When the face-up pile is placed at the bottom of the face-down pile, the situation becomes

	or in simplified form
$37 - X$ cards	
$X - 1$ cards	
Chosen card	36 cards
$15 - X$ cards	Chosen card
	$15 - X$ cards

Spelling out the phrase *I wish all my card tricks worked this easily*, which has 36 letters, and dealing one card for each letter, will use all of the cards above the chosen card. When the next card is turned over, it will be the one remembered.

Card Trick 15

A Personalised Card Trick

Let the name of the volunteer have X letters.

Spelling out the phrase *this is a ---------- ---------- card trick* will use $16 + X$ cards.

Let the number of cards removed be Y, leaving $16 + X - Y$ cards in the packet to be used.

When the ten cards are dealt face-up, the remembered card will be the Yth card dealt and so will have $Y - 1$ cards below it.

If this packet is then turned over and then replaced on top of the remaining cards in the initial packet of cards being used for the trick, the remembered card will then be the Yth card from the top and so have $Y - 1$ cards above it.

The phrase *---------- ---------- will be astonished* also has $16 + X$ letters and so, dealing one card per letter as you spell out the phrase will use up the whole of the packet and leave $16 + X - (16 + X - Y) = Y$ letters still to be accounted for. When the dealt cards are turned over, the remembered card will still be the Yth card from the top and so will be the final card dealt.

Card Trick 16
Unbelievable Mathematical Manipulation!

This trick is an example of a general principle which I will attempt to prove.

If a packet of n cards is taken and X cards dealt from the top of the face-down packet, the remaining $n - X$ cards placed on top of the dealt cards as a block and this process repeated twice more, then the bottom card of the original n card packet will rise to the top provided $X \geq n/2$.

Let the number of cards dealt on top of the chosen card be $n - 1$ and let the number of cards dealt each time be X.

The relative position of the chosen card after each deal is shown in the table below.

Initial position	Position after 1 deal and drop	Position after 2 deals and drops	Position after 3 deals and drops
$n - 1$ cards	$n - 1 - X$ cards	X cards	Chosen card
Chosen card	Chosen card	Chosen card	$n - 1$ cards
	X cards	$n - 1 - X$ cards	

The key point for the trick to work is that the chosen card needs to be one of the cards dealt on the second deal. This will occur if

$$X \geq n - 1 - X + 1 \quad \Rightarrow \quad X \geq n - X \quad \Rightarrow \quad 2X \geq n \quad \Rightarrow \quad X \geq n/2$$

In this case, the number of cards dealt each time is 12, while the total number of cards is between 13 and 22. Because $12 \geq 22/2$, the trick will work automatically as shown above.

To vary the trick, you could ask a volunteer for their favourite word of about ten letters at the start of the trick and use this word three times as the magic word. If you do that you would need to be careful about the number of cards dealt on top of their chosen card. This number must be at least as big as the length of the word to be used and strictly less than twice as long.

Card Trick 17

A Simple 21 Card Trick

Although the title of this trick is "A Simple 21 Card Trick", the simplicity lies in performing the trick rather than in the mathematics underlying it. The trick itself is fairly well known but I would guess that most people who perform it are not aware of why it actually works. In fact the key mathematical process involved is quite sophisticated and is known as a contraction mapping*.

Assume the chosen card was initially the Xth card in the face-down packet before the cards are first dealt into three columns. Once the card is identified and the cards picked up with the column containing the chosen card as the middle column, the position of the card within the packet will have changed to become the Yth card in the face-down packet. There is a mathematical relationship between X and Y that can be expressed in the form

$$Y = 7 + [X/3]$$

where $[X/3]$ is the smallest whole number greater than or equal to X/3.

There is always one complete column of cards (seven cards in total) above the chosen card which explains the "7" in the formula. The position of the card within its column can be related to its initial position in the packet by noting that the 1st, 2nd and 3rd cards in the packet all become the 1st cards in their columns, the 4th, 5th and 6th cards in the packet all become the 2nd cards in their columns etc. Mathematically this is equivalent to saying that the Xth card in the packet becomes the $[X/3]^{th}$ card in its column, giving the total formula relating the positions of the cards before they are dealt and after one deal and gathering as the one given above.

Repeating this process will further contract the range of positions within the pack that the chosen card can actually take until, after three deals, the chosen card will always be the middle card (the 11th) of the packet as shown in the table below. Here, the columns headed "Position after j deals (Y_j)" refer to the position of the card after j sets of dealing <u>and</u> regathering.

Initial position (X)	Position after 1 deal (Y_1)	Position after 2 deals (Y_2)	Position after 3 deals (Y_3)
1, 2, 3	8	10	11
4, 5, 6	9	10	11
7, 8, 9	10	11	11
10, 11, 12	11	11	11
13, 14, 15	12	11	11
16, 17, 18	13	12	11
19, 20, 21	14	12	11

Similar tricks can be carried out with any number of cards M provided M = p × q where p and q are both odd numbers and the cards are dealt into p columns of q cards each. The general mapping to find the position of a card that is originally the Xth card in the packet after one set of dealing and gathering, when the chosen column is always placed as the middle column of the reformed packet, is

$$Y = ((p - 1) \times q)/2 + [X/p].$$

This process will take n deals to converge to the middle card of the packet (which will be the $(p \times q + 1)/2^{th}$ card) where n is the smallest whole number satisfying the inequality

$$q/p^{n-1} \leq 1.$$

For example, consider using 35 cards. If they are dealt into five columns of seven, then three sets of dealing and gathering are required to isolate the chosen card as the middle or 18th card in the packet. However if they are dealt into seven columns of five, then only two sets of dealing and gathering are required to isolate the chosen card as the 18th card in the packet.

*A contraction mapping is a function f acting on a set S such that $\exists$ K with $0 < K < 1$
and $|f(X) - f(Y)| \leq K|X - Y|$ for X, Y $\in$ S.
The Banach Fixed Point Theorem for contraction mappings states that every such mapping will always have a fixed point such that $f(p) = p$.

Card Trick 18

A 49 Card Trick

Tricks involving repeated dealing of cards into columns work most easily and rapidly when the number of cards involved is a square number. This is because when you have a square number of cards the cards in any one column after one deal will automatically be a row of cards on the next deal.

In this trick, the chosen column after the first deal is picked up 4th which forces the chosen card to be in the 4th row when the cards are gathered and redealt. Picking up the chosen column after the second deal first then forces the chosen card to be the 4th card from the top of the face-down pack.

Moving three cards secretly from the top of the pack to the bottom will then leave the chosen card as the top card of the pile from where it can be manipulated as required.

Card Trick 19

A 36 Card Trick

As mentioned in the previous trick, square numbers of cards are most easily manipulated. The mathematics of this trick allows you to carry it out without even touching or seeing the cards, provided your volunteer follows your instructions carefully.

Assume you are told that the chosen card is in column A after one deal. When the cards are gathered up and re-dealt, this will force the chosen card to be the Ath card dealt in its new column and so will have $A - 1$ cards above it in that column. When you are then told that the chosen card is actually in column B, you now know exactly where the card is, namely the Ath card down column B.

When the cards are gathered again and the pack turned over, there will be $B - 1$ columns of cards above the chosen column plus a further $A - 1$ cards above the chosen card. This makes a total of $6(B - 1) + A - 1 = A + 6B - 7$ cards above the chosen card.

If $X = A + 6B - 6$, then dealing $X - 1 = A + 6B - 7$ cards will use up the cards above the chosen cards leaving the next card as the chosen card.

If 25 cards in five columns of five cards or 49 cards in seven columns of seven are used, simply replace the 6 in the above proof by 5 or 7 respectively.

Card Trick 20

A 27 Card Trick

When the number of cards used is not a square number, the process of identifying the card becomes a much more difficult process. Most of the mathematics required to explain this trick, and the next two tricks, was derived from an article by C. J. Priday I found in an old issue of the Mathematical Gazette called "Card Tricks for Christmas" (Priday (1972)).

Let P_0 be the position of the card that will be chosen before any cards have been dealt out and let P_1 be its position after the cards have been dealt out into columns and picked up once.

Assume the card is identified as being in column A.

Then P_1 is related to P_0 via the formula

$$P_1 = 9(A - 1) + (P_0 - A)/3 + 1.$$

This occurs because the chosen card will have $A - 1$ columns above it, consisting of $9(A - 1)$ cards, plus the cards above it in its own column. Now the 1st, 2nd and 3rd cards originally will have 0 cards above them in columns 1, 2 and 3 respectively, the 4th 5th and 6th cards originally will have one card above them in columns 1, 2 and 3 respectively etc. so it can be seen that the number of cards above the chosen card in its column will be $(P_0 - A)/3$. Thus, as there are $9(A - 1) + (P_0 - A)/3$ cards above the chosen card, adding 1 to this will give its position and so its position must be given by the formula for P_1 above.

Now $\qquad P_1 = 9(A - 1) + (P_0 - A)/3 + 1 \quad \Rightarrow \quad 3P_1 = 27A - 27 + P_0 - A + 3$

or $\qquad 3P_1 = 26A - 24 + P_0$

Similarly $\qquad P_2 = 9(B - 1) + (P_1 - B)/3 + 1 \qquad \Rightarrow \qquad 3P_2 = 26B - 24 + P_1$

$\qquad\qquad P_3 = 9(C - 1) + (P_2 - C)/3 + 1 \qquad \Rightarrow \qquad 3P_3 = 26C - 24 + P_2$

where P_2 and P_3 are the positions of the chosen card after two and three deals and pick-ups respectively and B and C are the numbers of the columns in which the chosen card lies. Eliminating P_1 and P_2 from these equations, we obtain

$$27P_3 = 9(26C - 24) + 3(26B - 24) + (26A - 24) + P_0$$

or

$$27P_3 = 26(9C + 3B + A - 12) + P_0 \quad = 27X + P_0 - X$$

where X is defined using the formula $\qquad X = 9C + 3B + A - 12.$

Dividing through by 27 now gives

$$P_3 = X + (P_0 - X)/27$$

Now $1 \le P_0 \le 27$ and $1 \le X \le 27$

so $-26 \le P_0 - X \le 26 \Rightarrow -26/27 \le (P_0 - X)/27 \le 26/27.$

As P_3 and X are both integers, $(P_0 - X)/27$ must also be an integer and the only possible integer value it can take is zero i.e. $P_0 = X$.

This implies that $P_3 = X$ and so the position of the chosen card after three sets of dealing and gathering is given by $P_3 = 9C + 3B + A - 12$.

An interesting corollary of this proof, because $P_3 = X$ and $P_0 = X$, is that $P_0 = P_3$. In other words, after three deals the original order of the cards has been restored.

Thus, dealing $X - 1$ cards will use up the cards above the chosen card, meaning that the next card dealt will be the chosen card.

Card Trick 21

A Harder 21 Card Trick

The mathematics for this trick is very similar to the previous trick, although there is an added complication which produces the correction term in the formula.

Let P_0 be the position of the card that will be chosen before any cards have been dealt out and let P_1 be its position after the cards have been dealt out into columns and picked up once.

Assume the card identified as being in column A.

Then, in a similar way to that explained in the previous trick, P_1 is related to P_0 via the formula

$$P_1 = 7(A - 1) + (P_0 - A)/3 + 1 \quad \Rightarrow \quad 3P_1 = 21A - 21 + P_0 - A + 3$$

or $\qquad 3P_1 = 20A - 18 + P_0$

Similarly $\qquad P_2 = 7(B - 1) + (P_1 - B)/3 + 1 \qquad \Rightarrow \qquad 3P_2 = 20B - 18 + P_1$

$$P_3 = 7(C - 1) + (P_2 - C)/3 + 1 \qquad \Rightarrow \qquad 3P_3 = 20C - 18 + P_2$$

where P_2 and P_3 are the positions of the chosen card after two and three deals and pick-ups respectively. Eliminating P_1 and P_2 from these equations, we obtain

$$27P_3 = 9(20C - 18) + 3(20B - 18) + (20A - 18) + P_0$$

or

$$27P_3 = 20(9C + 3B + A - 12) + 6 + P_0 = 20X + 6 + P_0$$

where X is defined using the formula $\qquad X = 9C + 3B + A - 12.$

An alternative way of writing the previous expression for $27P_3$ is

$$27P_3 = 27X - 7X + 6 + P_0$$

Dividing through by 27 and rearranging now gives

$$P_3 = X - X/4 + k \qquad \text{or} \qquad P_3 = X - (X/4 - k)$$

where

$$k = \frac{P_0 + 6}{27} + \left(\frac{1}{4} - \frac{7}{27} \right) X = \frac{4P_0 + 24 - X}{108}$$

Now $\qquad 1 \le P_0 \le 21$ and $1 \le X \le 27$

so $\qquad 1 \le 4P_0 + 24 - X \le 107 \Rightarrow 0 < k < 1.$

As P_3 and X are both integers, $(X/4 - k)$ must also be an integer and the only possible integer value it can take is $[X/4]$.

Thus, after three sets of dealing and gathering, the position of the chosen card within the pack is given by $\qquad P_3 = X - [X/4].$

Card Trick 22

A 52 Card Trick

Let P_0 be the position of the chosen card in the pack before any cards have been dealt out and let P_1 be the position of the card after the cards have been dealt into columns and picked up once.

Assuming A, B and C are the columns in which the chosen card appears after one, two and three deals respectively, then the position of the card after one deal and pick-up will be, by a similar argument to that in the previous two tricks

$$P_1 = 13 \times (\text{column} - 1) + \text{position in that column}$$

i.e. $$P_1 = 13 \times (A - 1) + (P_0 - A)/4 + 1$$

which simplifies to $\quad 4P_1 = 51A + P_0 - 48.$

Using similar definitions for P_2 and P_3 we can also show that

$$4P_2 = 51B + P_1 - 48 \quad \Rightarrow \quad 16P_2 = 4 \times 51B + 4P_1 - 4 \times 48$$

and

$$4P_3 = 51C + P_2 - 48 \quad \Rightarrow \quad 64P_3 = 16 \times 51C + 16P_2 - 16 \times 48$$

Eliminating P_1 and P_2 from these equations to get P_3 in terms of P_0 we obtain

$$64P_3 = 16(51C - 48) + 4(51B - 48) + 51A - 48 + P_0$$

or

$$64P_3 = 51(16C + 4B + A - 20) + 12 + P_0$$

$$64P_3 = 51X + 12 + P_0$$

or

$$64P_3 = 64X - 13X + 12 + P_0$$

when X is defined as $X = 16C + 4B + A - 20$ as suggested in the mechanics of the trick.

This can be rearranged to

$$P_3 = X - X/5 + k \quad \text{or} \quad P_3 = X - (X/5 - k) \quad (*)$$

where

$$k = \frac{P_1 + 12}{64} + \left(\frac{1}{5} - \frac{13}{64}\right)X = \frac{5P_1 + 60 - X}{320}$$

Now because $1 \le P_0 \le 52$ and $1 \le X \le 64$

$$65 \le 5P_0 + 60 \le 320 \quad \Rightarrow \quad 1 \le 5P_0 + 60 - X \le 319.$$

This means that $0 < k < 1.$

222

As P_3 and X are integers, (*) indicates that $(X/5 - k)$ must also be an integer and because we have $0 < k < 1$, it must equal $[X/5]$.

Therefore if $X = A + 4B + 16C - 20$, then the position of the chosen card within the pack after three sets of dealing and gathering, P_3, is given by $P_3 = X - [X/5]$ and so dealing out the cards as indicated in the description of the trick will reveal the chosen card.

Card Trick 23

A Harder 36 Card Trick

This trick has a similar explanation to Card Trick 19 except in this case, instead of finding the position of the chosen card after two deals by picking up the columns of cards in the order they are dealt and using the column number, the chosen column is picked up in a specific position after each deal to force the chosen card into a specific position in the packet.

Let the number called out be N

Aside: The secret step of calculating $N - 1$ and then finding out how many times 6 goes into $N - 1$ and what the remainder is to calculate your A and B respectively is equivalent to expressing $N - 1$ as AB in base 6.   i.e. $N - 1 = 6 \times A + B$

Remember, when you use a square number of cards for this sort of trick, every column automatically becomes a row after the cards are gathered and re-dealt. When the column containing the chosen card after one deal is picked up with B columns underneath it and the cards re-dealt, the chosen card will have B cards beneath it within its column. Then when the column containing the chosen card after this second deal is picked up with A columns underneath it, the chosen card will then have A columns worth of cards plus the B cards from its own column underneath it. i.e. there will be $6 \times A + B = N - 1$ cards beneath the chosen card.

When the reformed packet is turned over, there will then be $N - 1$ cards above the chosen card and so the chosen card will appear as the Nth card dealt.

A more general mathematical proof for similar tricks, first for dealing 27 cards into three columns of nine and then for dealing b^r cards into b columns of b^{r-1} can be found in the Mathematical Gazette article "The twenty-seven card trick" by Calvin T. Long (Long (1991)).

Card Trick 24

A Complete Deal

I found this trick and its explanation in an article called "A Mysterious Deal" by Michael Smith in Symmetry Plus magazine (Smith (1997)).

Initially consider one pile. If the value of the face-up card is X, then $12 - X$ cards will be dealt face-down onto the pile to complete it. This means that the completed pile will contain $1 + 12 - X = 13 - X$ cards.

Now consider the full situation.

Let the values of the face-up cards in the P completed piles be $X_1, X_2, ..., X_P$.

This means the number of cards in the completed piles is

$$13 - X_1 + 13 - X_2 + ... + 13 - X_P$$

and so we have

$$13 - X_1 + 13 - X_2 + ... + 13 - X_P + C = 52$$

$$\therefore \quad 13 \times P - (X_1 + X_2 + ... + X_P) + C = 52$$

$$\therefore \quad 13 \times P - 52 + C = X_1 + X_2 + ... + X_P$$

$$\therefore \quad 13 \times (P - 4) + C = (X_1 + X_2 + ... + X_P)$$

This tells us that the sum of the values of the face-up cards will be given by using the formula $13 \times (P - 4) + C$ as required.

Card Trick 25

Ten Is My Lucky Number

Let the values of the initial face-up cards of the three chosen piles be a, b and c.

Each pile consists of the initial card itself plus the extra cards dealt to take the value up to 13. Thus the total number of cards in the three piles is

$$T = 1 + 13 - a + 1 + 13 - b + 1 + 13 - c = 42 - a - b - c.$$

The number of cards remaining is $52 - (42 - a - b - c) = 10 + a + b + c$

Let X be the sum of the values of the initial cards from two of the chosen piles. Without losing any generality, I will take $X = a + b$.

Removing $X + 10$ cards from the remaining cards leaves
$10 + a + b + c - (10 + a + b) = c$ cards.

Thus, the number of cards remaining in your hand will equal the value of the initial card for the 3rd pile.

If four piles are chosen and the values of three top cards revealed, then the proof follows a very similar course although there are some special cases to be considered.

If the values of the initial face-up cards for the four chosen piles are a, b, c and d, the total number of cards in the four piles will be

$$T = 1 + 13 - a + 1 + 13 - b + 1 + 13 - c + 1 + 13 - d = 56 - a - b - c - d.$$

The number of cards remaining is $52 - (56 - a - b - c - d) = a + b + c + d - 4$

Note: this number could be zero, if all four chosen cards are aces. In this case, when you are told there are no spare cards, you can reveal that the top card of any chosen pile is an ace.

Assuming initially that the three cards revealed are not all aces and that X is the sum of the values of the initial cards from three of the chosen piles. Without losing any generality, I will take $X = a + b + c$.

Removing $X - 4$ cards from the remaining cards leaves
$a + b + c + d - 4 - (a + b + c - 4) = d$ cards.

Thus the number of cards remaining in your hand will equal the value of the initial card for the 4th pile.

If the three values revealed are all aces, $X - 4$ will be negative and so you should add 1 to the number of cards remaining to get the value of the initial card of the 4th pile.

Card Trick 26

A Hidden Card Revealed

The first important point is that the way you tell your volunteer to position their chosen card makes this card the 44th card in the face-down pack with only eight cards below it.

The way the dealing process works, a completed pile with a face-down card on the top will have 11 cards in it, whereas a pile with a face-up card on the top (where the final card dealt was equal to the number said) will have $11 - Y$ cards in it if Y is the value of the face-up card.

Let the values visible in the four piles be a, b, c and d where the value of any variable can be taken to be 0 if there is a face-down card on top of the pile.

The total number of cards in the four piles is

$$T = 11 - a + 11 - b + 11 - c + 11 - d = 44 - (a + b + c + d)$$

and the number of cards remaining in the pack will be

$$52 - (44 - (a + b + c + d)) = a + b + c + d + 8.$$

Taking X as the sum of the values of the visible cards, $X = a + b + c + d$ and so the total number of cards remaining in the pack will be $X + 8$. If X more cards are dealt from the remaining pack then only eight cards will be left. As the chosen card was initially positioned to be the 44th card with only eight cards below it, this means that the final card dealt will have been the chosen card.

Card Trick 27

Lucky 7

This trick is another I first saw in an article of the same name by Michael Smith in Symmetry Plus magazine (Smith (1996)).

Let the number chosen be N.

If N cards are discarded, there will be $52 - N$ cards remaining in the pack.

26 cards are dealt face-up and (secretly) the $N + 7^{th}$ card remembered. This means that there will be $N + 6$ cards above the card remembered when the packet of 26 cards is turned face-down and hence $52 - N + N + 6 = 32$ cards above the chosen card when the packet of 26 cards is placed at the bottom of the remaining cards. This makes the card remembered the 33rd card in the remaining pack.

Let the values of the face-up cards be a, b and c.

The total number of cards in the three piles, once the extra cards have been dealt onto the piles to take the totals up to 10, will be

$$1 + 10 - a + 1 + 10 - b + 1 + 10 - c = 33 - (a + b + c).$$

The total value of the face-up cards is $X = a + b + c$ and so dealing out $X - 1$ more cards will mean the total number of cards dealt will have been $33 - (a + b + c) + X - 1 = 32$. This means that the next card to be dealt will be the card you remembered.

Card Trick 28

Lucky 13

The secret step in this trick is designed to position the remembered card with ten cards on top of it in the face-up packet of dealt cards and so with ten cards below it when the packet of dealt cards is replaced at the bottom of the remaining pack. This makes the remembered card the 42nd card in the face-down pack.

This analysis seems to ignore the fact that there have been three cards selected from the remaining pack before the dealt cards were replaced on the bottom. However, these three cards are only selected when they are to eliminate any possibility of the card remembered being chosen or indeed any of the cards below it being chosen, which would change its position in the pack and render the trick invalid.

Let the values of the three chosen cards be a, b and c.

The total number of cards in the three piles, once the extra cards have been dealt onto the piles to take the totals up to 13, will be

$$1 + 13 - a + 1 + 13 - b + 1 + 13 - c = 42 - (a + b + c).$$

The total value of the face-up cards is $X = a + b + c$ and so dealing out $X - 1$ more cards will mean the total number of cards dealt will have been $42 - (a + b + c) + X - 1 = 41$. This means that the next card to be dealt will be the card you remembered.

Card Trick 29

Jack!

Although the trick itself is very straightforward to perform, the maths behind it is actually quite fiddly to explain.

In the trick, cards are repeatedly being moved from the back of the packet to the front (from your perspective). As the Jack starts as the closest card to you, it will be the 7th and 14th and 21st card etc. to be moved.

When attempting to reveal the Jack, cards are moved in multiples of the number called out, with the last card of those moved being revealed each time. The number called out is specified to be between 2 and 6.

Let the number called out be q.
To reveal the Jack, we require a multiple of q to equal a multiple of 7

> i.e. $q \times m = 7 \times n$
> where m is the number of batches of q cards that are moved.

Now $2 \leq q \leq 6$ and so, because 7 is a prime number, the only way the left hand side can be a multiple of 7, is for m to also be a multiple of 7. The simplest case of this occurs when m = 7, implying that the Jack will be the 7th card to be examined.

This tells us that the earliest that the Jack can be revealed is after six other cards have been examined. However, we have not yet shown that this will mean that all the other cards will have been revealed first, as we could have finished on the same card more than once.

In fact this is impossible because to do so would imply moving a multiple of seven cards, q cards at a time, in fewer than seven sets and we have just shown that this does not happen. This means that before any card can be the final card on two occasions, all of the other cards must have been the final card once.

Thus the Jack will always be the last card to be revealed.

The more general situation has p cards in the packet, where p is a prime number, and has the number called out (and hence the number of cards moved each time) q is in the range $2 \leq q \leq p - 1$. To reveal the Jack, we require a multiple of q to equal a multiple of p

> i.e. $q \times m = p \times n$
> where m is the number of batches of q cards that are moved.

The argument now follows exactly the same path as the one above, implying that m must be equal to p to reveal the Jack for the first time and that when this does occur, all the other cards will already have been revealed.

Card Trick 30

Double Dealing

Let the number of cards in each of the two piles be Y.

Let the number of cards cut by the second volunteer from the second pile be X.

When the piles are combined to a single pile, the cards are arranged in the following way:

$$X - 1 \text{ cards}$$
$$\text{Chosen card}$$
$$Y - 1 \text{ cards}$$
$$\text{Chosen card}$$
$$Y - X \text{ cards}$$

The top Y cards from the combined pile are then dealt face-down leaving the two piles arranged as follows:

$Y - X$ cards	$X - 1$ cards
Chosen card	Chosen card
$X - 1$ cards	$Y - X$ cards

If the second pile is turned over so that it is face up, the chosen card that is in that pile will be Y – X cards from the top, which is the same position as the chosen card in the first pile. Thus both chosen cards will appear at the same time and so, when one chosen card is dealt from the top of the face-up pile, the corresponding card at the top of the face-down pile will be the other chosen card.

Card Trick 31

Four Into Three Does Go!

Assume that the cards have been dealt into four equal piles, the chosen card placed on top of one of the piles and the piles gathered into a single packet. The key to the trick is that the chosen card is in the centre of this packet. The analysis below follows the structure suggested by Markovitz (1983).

Let the number of cards in the packet be t.

Let the number of cards above and including the middle card of the packet be m.

Let the number of the pile into which the last card is dealt be i   i = 1, 2 or 3.

Let the number of cards in the pile which has the last card dealt be k.

Because the chosen card is the centre card in the packet $m = (t + 1)/2$.

The cards are being dealt into three piles and so $t = 3(k - 1) + i$

Combining these two expressions we have $m = (3k - 3 + i + 1)/2$

Note the fact that m must be a whole number and then consider the situation that occurs for each value of i in turn. The aim is to show which pile contains the mth card when the cards are dealt into three piles and also that the mth card becomes the middle card of that pile.

Consider the situation when the final card is dealt into the 1st pile.

$$i = 1: \quad \therefore \quad m = (3k - 3 + 1 + 1)/2 = (3k - 1)/2.$$

For this to be a whole number, k most be an odd number i.e. $k = 2u + 1$ for some integer u.

$$\therefore \ m = (3(2u + 1) - 1)/2 = (6u + 3 - 1)/2 = (6u + 2)/2 = 3u + 1$$
$$\Rightarrow \text{ the middle card is dealt into the } 1^{st} \text{ pile}$$

$\therefore$ If the final card is dealt into the 1st pile, retain the 1st pile as this contains the original middle card.

$$k = 2u + 1 \ \Rightarrow \text{ middle card of this pile has u cards below it}$$
but $m = 3u + 1 \Rightarrow$ the original middle card will have u cards below it when it is dealt into the 1st pile. i.e. the original middle card of the whole packet has become the middle card of its new pile.

In a similar way, consider the situation when the final card is dealt into the 2nd pile.
$$i = 2: \ m = (3k - 3 + 2 + 1)/2 = (3k)/2.$$

For this to be a whole number, k must be an even number i.e. $k = 2v$ for some integer v.

$$\therefore \ m = (3(2v))/2 = (6v)/2 = 3v$$

232

$\Rightarrow$ the middle card is dealt into the 3rd pile.

$\therefore$ If the final card is dealt into the 2nd pile, retain the 3rd pile as this contains the original middle card.

$k = 2v \Rightarrow 2^{nd}$ pile has $2v$ cards in it $\Rightarrow 3^{rd}$ pile will have $2v - 1$ cards in it

$\therefore$ the middle card of the 3rd pile will have $v - 1$ cards below it

but $\quad m = 3v \Rightarrow$ the original middle card will have $v - 1$ cards below it when it is dealt into the 3rd pile. i.e. the original middle card of the whole packet has become the middle card of its new pile.

Again in a similar way, consider the situation when the final card is dealt into the 3rd pile

$$i = 3 : \quad m = (3k - 3 + 3 + 1)/2 = (3k + 1)/2.$$

For this to be a whole number, k must be an odd number i.e. $k = 2w + 1$ for some integer u.

$\therefore \ m = (3(2w + 1) + 1)/2 = (6w + 3 + 1)/2 = (6w + 4)/2 = 3w + 2$

$\Rightarrow$ the middle card is dealt into the 2nd pile.

$\therefore$ If the final card is dealt into the 3rd pile, retain the 2nd pile.

$k = 2w + 1 \Rightarrow$ the middle card of this pile has w cards below it

but $\quad m = 3w + 2 \Rightarrow$ the original middle card will have w cards below it when it is dealt into the 2nd pile. i.e. the original middle card of the whole packet has become the middle card of its new pile.

The middle card of the original packet has become the middle card of the appropriately selected packet, allowing the process to be repeated until a single card remains. This will be the middle card of the original packet and hence be the chosen card.

Card Trick 32

Talking Cards

When I first saw this trick, courtesy of Cliff Daniel at the end of a session at the British Congress of Mathematics Education – 6, I could not see how it could possibly work. There did not seem to be sufficient steps to isolate the chosen cards but, when you look at it mathematically, the reason it works does become clear. I will give two proofs here – the first for the specific situation mentioned in the text describing the trick and the second for the more general situation where the two extra Queens have been positioned in different places. The key to the trick is that, when the pack is cut, the first cut must be between the two extra Queens and the second cut must be after the second Queen. Provided this occurs, the trick will always work.

In the specific situation described in the text, the extra Queens are placed as the 10th and 29th cards of the 54 card face-down pack. This means that there are nine cards before the first Queen, 18 cards between the Queens and 25 cards after the second Queen.

As the key fact mentioned above must hold for the trick to work, let us assume that the first card cut is X cards after the first Queen and the second card cut is Y cards after the second Queen. This means that the situation after the cuts identifying the chosen cards is as follows:

Pile 1	Pile 2	Pile 3
9 cards	$18 - X$ cards	$25 - Y$ cards
Queen	Queen	
$X - 1$ cards	$Y - 1$ cards	
Chosen card	Chosen card	

When the pack is reformed with Pile 2 on top, then Pile 1 and Pile 3 on the bottom, the new pack consists of

$18 - X$ cards
Queen
$Y - 1$ cards
Chosen card
9 cards
Queen
$X - 1$ cards
chosen card
$25 - Y$ cards

Removing the Queens then gives

Pile A	Pile B	Pile C
$18 - X$ cards	$Y - 1$ cards	$X - 1$ cards
	Chosen card	Chosen card
	9 cards	$25 - Y$ cards

234

And reforming this pack with Pile A on top, then Pile C and Pile B on the bottom gives us

18 – X cards	or in simplified form
X – 1 cards	
Chosen card	17 cards
25 – Y cards	Chosen card
Y – 1 cards	24 cards
Chosen card	Chosen card
9 cards	9 cards

As can be seen, the chosen cards are now the 18th and the 43rd cards in the pack as claimed.

In the more general case where the two Queens are the Pth and Q^{th} cards in the 54-card face-down pack, provided the cuts are between the Queens and after the second Queen respectively, the maths works in a very similar way. After the cuts identifying the chosen cards we have the following situation:

Pile 1	Pile 2	Pile 3
P – 1 cards	Q – P – 1 – X cards	54 – Q – Y cards
Queen	Queen	
X – 1 cards	Y – 1 cards	
Chosen card	Chosen card	

When the pack is reformed with Pile 2 on top, then Pile 1 and Pile 3 on the bottom, the new pack consists of

Q – P – 1 – X cards
Queen
Y – 1 cards
Chosen card
P – 1 cards
Queen
X – 1 cards
Chosen card
54 – Q – Y cards

Removing the Queens then gives

Pile A	Pile B	Pile C
Q – P – 1 – X cards	Y – 1 cards	X – 1 cards
	Chosen card	Chosen card
	P – 1 cards	54 – Q – Y cards

And reforming this pack with Pile A on top, then Pile C and Pile B on the bottom gives us

Q – P – 1 – X cards	or in simplified form
X – 1 cards	
Chosen card	
54 – Q – Y cards	Q – P – 2 cards
Y – 1 cards	Chosen card
Chosen card	53 – Q cards
P – 1 cards	Chosen card
	P – 1 cards

In the more general case, this makes the chosen cards the $(Q - P - 1)^{th}$ and the $(53 - P)^{th}$ cards in the pack, allowing you to vary the trick by placing the extra Queens in different positions in the pack.

That these formulae do work can be seen by considering the specific situation given in the trick. If P = 10 and Q = 29, the formulae above suggest that the chosen cards should be at positions Q – P – 1 = 29 – 10 – 1 = 18 and 53 – P = 53 – 10 = 43 and these were indeed the values shown in the initial part of the proof.

Card Trick 33
I'll Feel It In My Fingers!

Let the number of cards removed by the volunteer be X.

This means that the remembered card will be the Xth card dealt and so will have $X - 1$ cards below it and $20 - X$ cards above it in the face-up pile. This arrangement will swap over when the pile of cards is turned over later in the trick to leave $X - 1$ cards above the chosen card in the face-down pile.

The number of cards still in the pile in your hand is now $52 - X - 20 = 32 - X$.

Let the number called out be N.

When N cards are dealt, the number of cards still in your hand is now $32 - X - N$.

The pile of 20 cards is now turned over and the pack reformed with the pile of N cards on the bottom then the 20 cards containing the remembered card and finally the unused cards from your hand on top.

This means that there will be $32 - X - N + X - 1 = 31 - N$ cards above the remembered card in the reformed pack. Therefore, to isolate the remembered card, you need to move $32 - N$ cards with the last card being the one required.

Counting from $20 + N + 1$ up to 52 will move a total of $52 - (20 + N) = 32 - N$ cards which is exactly what is required.

To make this trick seem more mysterious, you could claim to be failing to feel any card heating up as you move the cards and stop trying once you have moved the required number of cards. A quick glance at the bottom card as you recombine the pack will tell you what the remembered card is and you can then pretend to be reading minds to narrow the choice of card down to the required card.

Card Trick 34

Third Time Lucky

Let the first number chosen be X.

Dealing X cards face-down onto the table, leaves the following situation:

$$X - 1 \text{ cards} \qquad\qquad 52 - X \text{ cards}$$
$$\text{Predicted card}$$

When the two piles are reformed, the situation becomes

$$X - 1 \text{ cards}$$
$$\text{Predicted card}$$
$$52 - X \text{ cards}$$

Let the second number chosen be Y (where Y > X).

Dealing Y cards face-down on the table, leaves the following situation:

$$Y - X \text{ cards} \qquad\qquad 52 - Y \text{ cards}$$
$$\text{Predicted card}$$
$$X - 1 \text{ cards}$$

When the two piles are reformed, the situation becomes

$$Y - X \text{ cards}$$
$$\text{Predicted card}$$
$$X - 1 \text{ cards}$$
$$52 - Y \text{ cards}$$

Dealing Y – X cards from the top of the pack will then reveal the predicted card.

Card Trick 35

Reading Minds

Let the number chosen by the volunteer be X.

Let the number of cards dealt be Y.

When these Y cards have been dealt, the face-up pile will have the following structure:

$$Y - X \text{ cards}$$
$$\text{Chosen card}$$
$$X - 1 \text{ cards}$$

The three piles then formed have the cards arranged in the following way:

face-down	face-up	in hand
X cards	Y − X cards Chosen card X − 1 cards	52 − X − Y cards

When the piles are gathered together in the indicated way, the pile will have the following structure:

52 − X − Y cards
X − 1 cards
Chosen card
Y − X cards
X cards

or in simplified form

51 − Y cards
Chosen card
Y cards

This has made the chosen card the $(52 - Y)^{\text{th}}$ card in the face-down pack and so it can be revealed as indicated.

Card Trick 36

Mental Agility

Let the number chosen be X.

The initial position after the card is chosen is as follows:

$$X - 1 \text{ cards}$$
$$\text{Chosen card}$$
$$52 - X \text{ cards}$$

Reversing 19 cards will change the arrangement to

$$19 - X \text{ cards}$$
$$\text{Chosen card}$$
$$X - 1 \text{ cards}$$
$$33 \text{ cards}$$

This has put the chosen card as the $(20 - X)^{\text{th}}$ card in the pack.

Counting on from $X + 1$ to 20, dealing one card each time, will mean that $20 - X$ cards will be dealt and so the final card dealt will be the one chosen.

In the variation, a number from 15 to 20 is called out.
Let this number be Y.

The initial position after the card is chosen is as follows:

$$X - 1 \text{ cards}$$
$$\text{Chosen card}$$
$$52 - X \text{ cards}$$

Reversing $Y - 1$ cards will change the arrangement to

$$Y - 1 - X \text{ cards}$$
$$\text{Chosen card}$$
$$X - 1 \text{ cards}$$
$$53 - Y \text{ cards}$$

This has put the chosen card as the $(Y - 1 - X)^{\text{th}}$ card in the pack.

Counting on from $X + 1$ to Y, dealing one card each time, will mean that $Y - X$ cards will be dealt and so the final card dealt will be the one chosen.

Card Trick 37

A Cool Card Trick

Let the number chosen be X.

The initial position when the two piles are dealt is

X cards   X cards
Chosen card

When the pile containing the chosen card is recombined with the remaining cards, the position becomes

X cards
Chosen card
$51 - 2X$ cards

Reversing the top 15 cards then gives the following arrangement:

$14 - X$ cards   or in simplified form
Chosen card
X cards $14 - X$ cards
$37 - X$ cards   Chosen card
                       37 cards

When the removed pile of X cards is returned to the top of the pile, the arrangement becomes

X cards   or in simplified form
$14 - X$ cards
Chosen card   14 cards
37 cards   Chosen card
                       37 cards

This makes the chosen card the 15th in the pack and so using a phrase like *A Cool Card Trick*, which has 14 letters, and dealing one card for each letter will allow the chosen card to be revealed as described.

If Y cards are reversed during the secret step instead of 15 cards, then the situation after that reversal will be as follows

$Y - 1 - X$ cards   or in simplified form
Chosen card
X cards $Y - 1 - X$ cards
$52 - Y - X$ cards   Chosen card
                     $52 - Y$ cards

This situation will be possible, provided $Y - 1 - X \geq 0$ and, as X is unknown but between 1 and 10 inclusive, taking $Y > 10$ will ensure the trick works.

When the removed pile of X cards is returned to the top of the pile, the arrangement becomes

X cards

Y − 1 − X cards

Chosen card

52 − Y cards

or in simplified form

Y − 1 cards

Chosen card

52 − Y cards

This has put the chosen card as the Yth card in the pack and so spelling out a phrase with Y − 1 letters in it and then turning over the next card will reveal the chosen card

Card Trick 38

The Ten Card Line

The key to this trick is that the cards are arranged in numerical order and so you always know where the 10 is before the volunteer moves a card.

Initially the cards are arranged   A   2   3   4   5   6   7   8   9   10.

You move two cards to demonstrate leaving 3   4   5   6   7   8   9   10   A   2.

This leaves the 10 as the 3rd card from the right (position 3) before your volunteer moves any cards with the Ace in position 2 and the 2 in position 1 – a fact you are aware of but your volunteer is not.

Let us assume that k cards are moved from left to right, where initially k < 8 to ease the analysis. The 10 will then be in position k + 3 and the Ace in position k + 2 with the cards then increasing in value as they go from left to right. The card in position 3 will be 1 + (k − 1) = k and so revealing the 3rd card will then tell you how many cards have been moved.

The only alteration to this analysis that needs to be made if k = 8 or k = 9, is that, because there will only ever be ten cards in the line, a card's position can be considered as

         position after move = position before move + k (mod 10).

This allows the extension to k = 8 and k = 9 and to the situation where the 10 no longer starts in the 3rd position, as will be the case after one volunteer has moved some cards. Having revealed the value of k in the initial trick, you are now aware that the 10 has moved to position k + 3 and so, if m cards are moved on the second occasion, revealing the value of the card at position k + 3 (mod 10) will then give the value of m by a similar analysis.

Card Trick 39

Magic Spelling

Let us assume that you have 13 clubs in your hand face down and you start to spell out ACE, putting the first three cards to the bottom of the pack as you spell out the word. If you are going to reveal the Ace when you turn over the fourth card then, fairly obviously, the Ace must have started as the fourth card down. It is then possible to continue this process identifying the position of each card in turn so that they appear at the appropriate stage.

Assume the cards are in the order   a b c d e f g h i j k l m   with a as the top card in the face-down pile in your hand.

As discussed earlier, if the Ace is to appear on cue, then card d must have been the Ace.

Before starting to spell out TWO the order now is   e f g h i j k l m a b c so h = TWO

If we continue this process we have

i j k l m a b c e f g	so a = THREE
b c e f g i j k l m	so g = FOUR
i j k l m b c e f	so m = FIVE
b c e f i j k l	so f = SIX
i j k l b c e	so c = SEVEN
e i j k l b	so b = EIGHT
e i j k l	so l = NINE
e i j k	so k = TEN
e i j (e i)	so i = JACK
j e (j e j e)	so e = QUEEN
	and hence j = KING

Thus to produce all the cards on cue, having spelt out the word and then turned over the next card, the original order of the cards needed to have been

$$3 \ 8 \ 7 \ A \ Q \ 6 \ 4 \ 2 \ J \ K \ 10 \ 9 \ 5$$

If instead of spelling out the word and then turning over the next card to reveal the required card, the card corresponding to the final letter of the word spelt was to be revealed, a slightly different order of cards is required. As before, assume the cards are in the order   a b c d e f g h i j k l m   with a as the top card in the face-down pile in your hand.

If the Ace is to appear on cue, then it is obvious that card c must have been the Ace. Before starting to spell out TWO the order now is   d e f g h i j k l m a b   so   f = TWO

244

If we continue this process we have

g h i j k l m a b d e	so k = THREE
l m a b d e g h i j	so b = FOUR
d e g h i j l m a	so h = FIVE
i j l m a d e g	so l = SIX
m a d e g i j	so g = SEVEN
i j m a d e	so d = EIGHT
e i j m a	so m = NINE
a e i j	so i = TEN
j a e (j)	so j = JACK
a e (a e a)	so a = QUEEN
	and hence e = KING

Thus to produce all the cards on cue as the final letter of the word is spelt, the original order of the cards needed to have been

Q 4 A 8 K 2 7 5 10 J 3 6 9.

245

Card Trick 40

Stop!

The pack has been spilt so that the packet contains nine cards and the remainder of the pack contains 43 cards. The digit sum of the number of cards in the remainder of the pack is 7 and this will also be the final digit sum if the 43 cards are split into two or more groups, their digit sums found and then the sum of these digit sums found. The packet is then cut so that the 7 is on the top to make the value of the top card equal to the digit sum of the remainder of the pack.

The order of cards in the packet is then   7 8 9 A 2 3 4 5 6
i.e. moving n cards will make the first card $7 + n$ (mod 9).

Now assume n cards are moved from the packet to the remainder of the pack. The number of cards in the remainder of the pack will be $43 + n$ and the value of the top card of the packet would be $7 + n$ (mod 9).

Now the digit sum of a number, if the process is repeated until a single digit remains, is equal to its remainder when divided by 9 and this process is not altered by splitting the number up into smaller parts and finding the digit sums of these smaller parts first.
i.e. the digit sum of $43 + n = 7 + n$ (mod 9).

This makes the value of the stop card equal to the value of the digit sum of the remaining pack plus the added cards.

Card Trick 41

Skilful Shuffling

The mathematics behind this trick is quite involved and I have been unable to find a full mathematical proof. In his book "Aha! A two volume collection" (Gardner 2006), Martin Gardner gives an informal proof by induction of the first example, which I explain here, before illustrating a similar proof for the second example.

Assume the pack is arranged with cards alternating in colour, RBRBRBRB... As the top card is Red (R), the bottom card of the pile will be Black (B).

Then roughly half the pack is dealt face-down onto the table. Following this, the pile on the table and the pile remaining in hand will be riffle shuffled together. At this stage the piles will be arranged from the bottom as follows:

pile in hand	pile on table
:	:
R	B
B	R
R	B
B	R

Without losing any generality, we can assume that the first card that falls once these two piles are being riffle shuffled together will be from the left hand pile and so will be black. It can then be seen that the bottom card of each of the piles will be red and so whichever pile the second card then falls from, the first pair of cards will consist of one black and one red card. The process can then continue with either exactly the same initial condition if both cards came from the same pile or the exact reverse (i.e. a red card at the bottom of the left hand pile and a black card at the bottom of the right hand pile) if one card fell from each pile. The process can then be repeated, making each pair of cards a different colour throughout the riffle shuffled pack. Note that this does not imply that the cards will alternate in colour through the shuffled pack, as it is easy to see how two red cards, for example, could be shuffled on top of each other (two cards from the left hand pile followed by one card from the right hand pile) but only that every pair of cards will contain one card of each colour.

To demonstrate why the first variation on the trick works, consider the initial pack of cards arranged so that the suits form a repeating pattern, HCSDHCSDHCSDHCSD...

When roughly half the pack is dealt onto the table prior to riffle shuffling, the piles will be arranged from the bottom as follows:

pile in hand	pile on table
:	:
S	C
D	H
H	D
C	S
S	C
D	H

Without losing any generality, I will assume that the bottom card falls from the left hand pile. After that, the different possibilities for the first four cards are illustrated in the table below.

Card								
1st	D							
2nd	S				H			
3rd	C		H		S		C	
4th	H	H	C	C	C	C	S	S

As can be seen, whichever of the possible ways the first four cards fall, there will be one of each suit in the group of four cards. This process can then be repeated from the new position and, in exactly the same way, the situation will be repeated. As was the case with the previous example, the proof does not guarantee that the cards will always come out with the suits in a particular order but only that each successive group of four cards will contain one card of each suit.

Card Trick 42

You Do As I Do

This card trick is not mathematical! The key is that, when your volunteer cuts the pack, they will be placing the card you remembered from the bottom of the pack directly on top of their chosen card. Cutting the pack again is very unlikely to alter this situation and so you could tell them to cut the cards again so their chosen card seems to be even more lost within the other cards.

When you receive the pack back from them, your remembered card will still be directly above their chosen card allowing you to reveal it as your own.

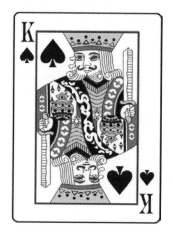

Appendix 1

The Chinese Remainder Theorem
or **How To Create Your Own Magic Trick**

Imagine the following problem:

I choose a number. Supposing I tell you that if I divide my number by 3, the remainder is 2, but if I divide my number by 5, the remainder is 4 and if I divide my number by 7, the remainder is 6, can you tell me what number I chose?

In actual fact, you can't be certain what number I chose as there are infinitely many numbers that will satisfy the conditions but, if I also tell you that the number I chose is the smallest one that satisfies the conditions, you might be able to work it out.

As it now stands, this turns out to be quite a simple problem, particularly if you notice that the remainders in each case are one less than the number I am dividing by. Hence, my number must be one less than a multiple of 3, one less than a multiple of 5 and one less than a multiple of 7. These three conditions mean my number is one less than a multiple of $3 \times 5 \times 7$ and, as it is the smallest possible number satisfying the conditions, it must be 104. (Check 104 does give the remainders stated!)

However, if I change things just a little bit, the problem suddenly becomes quite a lot harder as there is no quick trick to help you work out the number required. For example, consider this problem:

I choose a number. Supposing I tell you that if I divide my number by 3, the remainder is 2, but if I divide my number by 5, the remainder is 3 and if I divide my number by 7, the remainder is 2. What is the smallest number I could have chosen now?

This problem is the one generally quoted as being the one posed by Sun Tsu Suan-Ching in the 4th Century AD and is said to come from a Chinese general returning from battle and surveying his troops to see how many survived. Rather than counting them, the enterprising general is said to have got the troops to arrange themselves in groups of three, then groups of five and finally groups of seven, each time counting the troops left over. Presumably he then found a passing mathematician to help him set up equations and discover how many troops he had left. When you know the answer to the problem you will wonder why he bothered and didn't just count them, but that's how the story goes.

Both of the above problems are examples of applications of a theorem in Number Theory, known as the Chinese Remainder Theorem, which is what I am going to look at now.

The Chinese Remainder Theorem

Let m_1, m_2, ...m_n be a set of pairwise prime positive integers and let a_1, a_2, ...a_n be any integers. Then the system of simultaneous linear congruences $X \equiv a_1 \pmod{m_1}$

$$X \equiv a_2 \pmod{m_2}$$
$$\vdots$$
$$\vdots$$
$$X \equiv a_n \pmod{m_n}$$

has a unique solution between 0 and $M - 1$ where $M = m_1 m_2 \ldots m_n$ which is given by

$$X = a_1 b_1 M/m_1 + a_2 b_2 M/m_2 + \ldots + a_n b_n M/m_n \pmod{M}$$

where the b_i are determined from solving the equations $\qquad b_i M/m_i \equiv 1 \pmod{m_i}$.

This all looks quite complicated, particularly if you don't know a lot about modular arithmetic, but with a few explanations and examples it should become clearer.

Explanations

1. Pairwise prime numbers

Two positive integers are said to be co-prime if their highest common factor is 1. For example, 7 and 6 are co-prime (even though 6 is not a prime number) because the largest whole number that goes into both 7 and 6 is 1.
Three or more integers are pairwise prime if any two that can be chosen are co-prime. For example, 5, 6 and 7 are pairwise prime because 5 and 6, 6 and 7 and 5 and 7 are all co-prime.

2. Linear congruences and modular arithmetic

Modular arithmetic is essentially arithmetic of remainders and so expressions, or congruences, like $X \equiv 2 \pmod 3$ simply mean $X - 2$ (in this case) is an exact multiple of 3, the modulo of the problem. For example, $8 \equiv 2 \pmod 3$ because $8 - 2 = 6 = 2 \times 3$ and $11 \equiv 2 \pmod 3$ because $11 - 2 = 9 = 3 \times 3$. Similarly, if X is a multiple of 3 then dividing by 3 would leave no remainder and so we would have $X \equiv 0 \pmod 3$.

Two numbers a and b are said to be congruent (modulo m) if $a - b$ is and exact multiple of m. For example, from above, 8 and 11 are congruent modulo 3.

Example

Going back to our second problem (and Sun Tsu's original), we are trying to solve the simultaneous linear congruences $X \equiv 2 \pmod 3$, $X \equiv 3 \pmod 5$ and $X \equiv 2 \pmod 7$.

Using the Chinese Remainder Theorem we have $m_1 = 3$, $m_2 = 5$ and $m_3 = 7$ as our pairwise primes and $a_1 = 2$, $a_2 = 3$ and $a_3 = 2$ as the values our number leaves when divided by 3, 5 and 7 respectively. The value of the large number M is $M = 3 \times 5 \times 7 = 105$ and so the number we are looking for is given by

$$X = 2b_1 105/3 + 3b_2 105/5 + 2b_3 105/7 \pmod{105}$$

where
$$b_1 105/3 \equiv 1 \ (\text{mod } 3), \quad b_2 105/5 \equiv 1 \ (\text{mod } 5) \quad \text{and} \quad b_3 105/7 \equiv 1 \ (\text{mod } 7)$$

are the linear congruences we need to solve to be able to find our number.

Simplifying the arithmetic in these congruences gives

$$35b_1 \equiv 1 \ (\text{mod } 3), \quad 21b_2 \equiv 1 \ (\text{mod } 5) \text{ and } 15b_3 \equiv 1 \ (\text{mod } 7)$$

These congruences can be solved quite easily by simply substituting values and give

$$b_1 = 2, \ b_2 = 1 \text{ and } b_3 = 1$$

Check: $35 \times 2 = 70 = 3 \times 23 + 1, \ 21 \times 1 = 21 = 5 \times 4 + 1$ and $15 \times 1 = 15 = 7 \times 2 + 1$

Thus the number we are looking for is given by

$$X = 2 \times 2 \times 35 + 3 \times 1 \times 21 + 2 \times 1 \times 15 \ (\text{mod } 105)$$
$$\therefore X = 140 + 63 + 30 \ (\text{mod } 105)$$
$$\therefore X = 233 \ (\text{mod } 105)$$
$$\therefore X = 23$$

So the general turns out to have had only 23 soldiers left – surely it would have been quicker for him to have counted them rather than going through all this mathematical rigmarole, but why spoil a good story?

Proof of the Theorem

The full proof of the theorem is rather complicated so the version presented here has been simplified somewhat.
First, let us show that the value of X given does actually satisfy all the congruences. Remember

$$X = a_1 b_1 M/m_1 + a_2 b_2 M/m_2 + \ldots + a_n b_n M/m_n \ (\text{mod } M)$$

Now $M = m_1 m_2 \ldots m_n$ and so M/m_i will be a multiple of m_1 whenever $i \neq 1$. This means that $M/m_i \equiv 0 \ (\text{mod } m_1)$ and so $a_i b_i M/m_i \equiv 0 \ (\text{mod } m_1)$ for $i \neq 1$. Also, as b_1 was chosen specifically so that $b_1 M/m_1 \equiv 1 \ (\text{mod } m_1)$, we have (by multiplying both sides by a_1) that $a_1 b_1 M/m_1 \equiv a_1 \ (\text{mod } m_1)$ so that $X \equiv a_1 \ (\text{mod } m_1)$.

This argument can be repeated using m_2 instead of m_1, then m_3 instead of m_1, etc, and shows that $X \equiv a_i \ (\text{mod } m_i)$ for all i. Thus the value of X given in the theorem is a solution of the problem.

The next step is to show that the value of X this formula produces is the only one between 0 and $M - 1$ that satisfies the congruences. To do this, first assume there is another value Y that also satisfies all the congruences i.e. $Y \equiv a_1 \ (\text{mod } m_1), \ Y \equiv a_2 \ (\text{mod } m_2), \ \ldots, \ Y \equiv a_n \ (\text{mod } m_n)$.
This means that
$$X \equiv Y \ (\text{mod } m_1), \ X \equiv Y \ (\text{mod } m_2), \ \ldots, \ X \equiv Y \ (\text{mod } m_n) \text{ or}$$

253

$$X - Y \equiv 0 \ (\text{mod } m_1), \ X - Y \equiv 0 \ (\text{mod } m_2), \ \ldots, \ X - Y \equiv 0 \ (\text{mod } m_n)$$

But $X - Y \equiv 0 \ (\text{mod } m_1)$ means that $X - Y$ is a multiple of m_1, $X - Y \equiv 0 \ (\text{mod } m_2)$ means that $X - Y$ is a multiple of m_2, etc and so $X - Y$ must be a multiple of $m_1 m_2 \ldots m_n$ i.e. a multiple of M The only way this is possible with X and Y between 0 and $M - 1$ is if
$X - Y$ is 0 i.e. $X = Y$.

Thus the theorem is satisfied by the value of X given and that value is unique, completing the proof.

Constructing your own Magic Trick

After looking at all that theory, it is now time to show how the theory can be used to create seemingly magic tricks to amaze your friends. The key to creating the tricks is that you can decide on the values of m_1, m_2, $\ldots m_n$ beforehand (I usually stick to just three values to keep the trick fairly manageable) and so you can work out the values of b_1, b_2, $\ldots b_n$ and hence the rule for finding X before you start the trick.

Let us assume that you decide upon 7, 11 and 13 as your (pairwise) primes. To prepare your trick you now need to work out $M = 7 \times 11 \times 13 = 1001$ and the values of b_1, b_2 and b_3 for which
$$b_1(7 \times 11 \times 13)/7 \equiv 1 \ (\text{mod } 7),$$
$$b_2(7 \times 11 \times 13)/11 \equiv 1 \ (\text{mod } 11)$$
$$b_3(7 \times 11 \times 13)/13 \equiv 1 \ (\text{mod } 13)$$

i.e. solve $143b_1 \equiv 1 \ (\text{mod } 7)$, $91b_2 \equiv 1 \ (\text{mod } 11)$ and $77b_3 \equiv 1 \ (\text{mod } 13)$.

These congruences can be simplified by noting that (for example) when solving a congruence mod 7, any multiple of 7 can be subtracted from either side without affecting the result. So the equations to be solved simplify to

$$3b_1 \equiv 1 \ (\text{mod } 7), \ 3b_2 \equiv 1 \ (\text{mod } 11) \text{ and } 12b_3 \equiv 1 \ (\text{mod } 13)$$

which have solutions $b_1 = 5$, $b_2 = 4$ and $b_3 = 12$.
Check: $3 \times 5 = 15 \equiv 1 \text{ mod } 7$, $3 \times 4 = 12 \equiv 1 \text{ mod } 11$ and $12 \times 12 = 144 \equiv 1 \text{ mod } 13$
Thus the rule for calculating the number is
$X = 5 \times 143 \times R + 4 \times 91 \times S + 12 \times 77 \times T \ (\text{mod } 1001)$
or $X = 715R + 364S + 924T \ (\text{mod } 1001)$

where R, S and T are the remainders you get when the number chosen is divided by 7, 11 and 13 respectively.

Now you have the formula you need, you can then go out and perform your trick. Ask a member of the audience to choose any number between 1 and 1000. They now need to work out the remainders they get when they divide that number by 7, 11 and 13 respectively and tell you what they are (<u>in that order!</u>). If they have a calculator, you can speed things up by telling them to write the division as a top-heavy fraction and to tell you the second figure that appears once they press the = button. This will definitely work only when the numbers you choose for your pairwise primes are

254

actually prime numbers – in other situations they might have to think about the values that appear as the fraction part might have been cancelled down.

As an illustration, suppose the answers they give you are 4, 8 and 3.
Then, you work out $715 \times 4 + 364 \times 8 + 924 \times 3$ (mod 1001) = 8544 (mod 1001) $\equiv$ 536 and announce confidently that the number they chose was 536 and wait for the applause when you are proved correct. ($536/7 = 76\ \mathbf{4}/7$, $536/11 = 48\ \mathbf{8}/11$, $536/13 = 41\ \mathbf{3}/13$).

Like all good tricks, this does require you to do some preparation beforehand, but once that is done, you can go ahead and perform the trick over and over again without anyone knowing how you are doing it.

References

1. Acheson, D. J. *1089 and all that: A Journey into Mathematics*, Oxford University Press, Oxford (2002).

2. Adams, D. *The Hitchhiker's Guide to the Galaxy*, Pan Books, London (1979).

3. Barnard, T., "Less than 10p", Mathematics in School, **25(2)**, (1996) pp. 28-29.

4. Bizley, M. T. L., "A Christmas Party Piece", Mathematical Gazette, **59, No. 410**,(1975) pp. 264-266.

5. CIMT. "Choices", Mathematics Focus, **9,** (1993) p. 9, p. 19.

6. Eperson, D. B. "Puzzles, Pastimes, Problems", Mathematics in School, **14(4)**, (1985) pp. 16-17, 32-33.

7. Eperson, D. B. "Puzzles, Pastimes, Problems", Mathematics in School, **18(2)**, (1989) pp. 14-15, 38-39.

8. Eperson, D. B. "Puzzles, Pastimes, Problems", Mathematics in School, **19(3)**, (1990) pp. 20-21, 28-29.

9. Fraser, D. *Mathemagic,* Dale Seymour Publications, Palo Alto (1984).

10. Fulves, K. *Self Working Card Tricks*, Dover Publications, New York (1976).

11. Gardner, M. *Mathematics, Magic and Mystery*, Dover Publications, New York (1956).

12. Gardner, M. *The Mathematical Magic Show*, Penguin Books, London (1985).

13. Gardner, M *The Unexpected Hanging and Other Mathematical Diversions*, University of Chicago Press, Chicago (1991).

14. Gardner, M. *Aha! A two volume collection*, Mathematical Association of America (2006).

15. Long, C. T. "The 27 Card Trick", Mathematical Gazette, **175, No. 473,** (1991) pp. 300-302.

16. Lulli, H. "An Algebraic Puzzler", Mathematics Teacher, **77(9),** (1984) p. 688.

17. Markovitz, L. M. "Some Variations on a Mathematical Card Trick", Mathematics Teacher, **76(8),** (1983) pp. 618-619.

18. Priday, C. J. "Card Trick for Christmas", Mathematical Gazette, **156, No. 395,** (1972) pp. 18-19.

19. Simon, W. *Mathematical Magic*, Dover Publications, New York (1964).

20. Smith, M. "Playing Cards and Mathematics", Plus, **31,** (1995) p. 11.

21. Smith, M. "Lucky 7 – a Card Trick", Symmetry Plus, **1,** (1996) p. 2.

22. Smith, M. "A Mysterious Deal", Symmetry Plus, **4,** (1997) p. 8.

23. Stewart, I. *The Magical Maze*, Weidenfeld and Nicolson, London (1997).

On-line Articles

1. Mulcahay, C. (2004). "Low Down Triple Dealing", MAA Online. www.maa.org.

2. Colyvan, M. "Mathematical Magic",
   (http://owl.infosys.utas.edu.au/mathemagicians_circle/table4.html)

3. Peterson, I. "Alphamagic Squares", Science News Online, **164(1)** (2003).

Websites

1. www.card-trick.com

2. www.graphicsfactory.com

3. www.greenleecdscom/mathsdownloads.html

4. www.murderousmaths.co.uk

5. www.nrich.maths.org.uk